From Sunrise
to Sunset

A farm is an open book and anyone can read it. There have been many times in my life when I would have loved to have hidden a page or two of my "book", but mistakes can be seen for many months and are usually only removed by ploughing or the wonderful arrival of a new spring.

From Sunrise
to Sunset

A Farmer's Tale of Life in
Herefordshire and Yorkshire

WITH BEST WISHES

Trevor Robinson

Trevor Robinson

With illustrations by Simon Cooke
and a foreword by Ellen MacArthur DBE

From Sunrise to Sunset
Trevor Robinson

Published by Aspect Design 2015
Malvern, Worcestershire, United Kingdom.

Designed, printed and bound by Aspect Design
89 Newtown Road, Malvern, Worcs. WR14 1PD
United Kingdom
Tel: 01684 561567
E-mail: allan@aspect-design.net
Website: www.aspect-design.net

Cover Design Copyright © 2015 Aspect Design
Original image Copyright © 2015 Simon Cooke
ISBN 978-1-908832-71-9

Dedication and Acknowledgements

I dedicate this book to all farm workers
– the salt of the earth.

It was not until I sat down to write this section that I realised how many people have helped to get this small book into print – Geoffrey Barham for his persistence when I was flagging, Simon Cooke for his lovely drawings, Barbara Sykes of Freedom of Spirit and Border Collie Rescue in Yorkshire for reading the manuscript and giving me professional opinions (she has written 9 books on the Border Collie), Mick Hodgetts for working on many old photographs which Simon was able to work from, Sue Browning of Malvern for editing and correcting my dreadful spelling mistakes – and lastly, my wife Helen for her help and understanding!

Now, having got the script finished and all in order to go to the printers, I have got one last thing to do – try to get someone to write me a foreword – quite a tricky job! Well, as I have said many times in my book, often decisions just happen. So how did this decision come about? One day I was reading a magazine and the main article was an account of one of Dame Ellen MacArthur's epic journeys on the high seas. It was thrilling – this young, slight girl facing one challenge after another – the power of the sea – gales – hanging on for hours and hours under great strain with many of her aids going on the blink. At other times there was the joy of beautiful sunsets – calm seas – really good times – life was very good – so, looking back at the journey, the experience was a real mix of emotions and very satisfying with a strong feeling of achievement.

I began to see parallels with my life – hanging on for dear

life – when the bank could just cut me adrift to sink – could I hold on until the storm abated? Would I get stuck in the doldrums until money ran out? I also had wonderful times – a good crop – a good lambing – life was good. In seeing these parallels, I of course realised Dame Ellen had much, much more at stake. Where I would go back to being a farm worker, Ellen would be in dire straits! So with these thoughts on my mind, I decided to ask Dame Ellen to write my foreword. I could not believe my luck when she said that she would – it took a while to sink in – but I now have it and I am so grateful – thanks a lot, Ellen – you have made it all worthwhile.

Foreword

by Ellen MacArthur DBE

GROWING UP IN the countryside my childhood memories were built from a rich tapestry of moments, people, animals and pictures. Trevor's book plunged me straight back into that world, the sights, the sounds, the highs and the lows. I find myself inspired by his ability to endlessly graft, steadily and tirelessly building his dream, with his land around him. But when I read his words I find myself smiling, as, at the same time as whisking the reader back into a wonderful world of how things were, I am also reminded of what has not changed.

I too live on a farm, and the rhythm of the seasons, animals and sounds has, in my eyes, little changed. The delicate blankets of dew still return each year to cover the fields, and the characters still lean on the gates.

Long may that continue.....

Leominster

As the sun rose on the 25th of September in 1950 I became the proud tenant of Buckfield Farm, Leominster. My earlier years of being a farm worker and shepherd are recorded in *Working with the Curlew*. Those were the days before tractors, fertilisers and chemicals, but now farming was about to enter a period of fast progress – some of it too fast and in the wrong direction!

Buckfield Farm was thirty-two acres – enough in those days to support a newly married ex-farm worker and his lovely wife, Myfanwy. How lucky I was to realise my ambition and also get married in the space of six months. The farm was owned by Mr. Tom Rogers of Broadward Hall, Leominster, and he had been my last boss whilst I was a farm worker. I have been lucky in my life – working for people like Matt Middlemiss, Joe Downing and Tom Rogers – all men who knew their profession well and all of whom passed on their knowledge unstintingly. Indeed, it seemed that they really wanted their men to learn and be happy in their work. There were no secrets – it's very hard to hide things in farming – a farm is an open book and anyone can read it. There have been many times in my life when I would have loved to have hidden a page or two of my "book", but mistakes can be seen for many months and are usually only removed by ploughing or the wonderful arrival of a new spring.

During the years before, I had managed to scrape together a grand total of £500. This had been acquired by catching rabbits, working overtime for other farmers and being allowed to keep four sheep of my own in my boss's flock, but mainly from my last years' wages working for Mr. Tom Rogers.

My first day at Buckfield Farm I spent my £500! It was

to be many years before I again had £500. I bought, in September, ten in-calf Ayrshire heifers (young milking cows in calf for the first time). They were my chosen breed and were to be the foundation of my milking herd. Whilst working for Mr. Downing at Moss Hill Farm, Monkland, I had been in the Kingsland Young Farmers Club and we had been on visits to milking herds – both Ayrshire and Friesian. We also had to judge cattle at shows, so we'd had to learn about the finer points of the dairy cow. I had taken great interest in this because I thought that if I ever started farming I would have to milk as it is one of the few enterprises that gives a cheque every month (provided that milk is produced, of course!). So the more I could learn, the more milk I could get out of each cow. Many nights had been spent reading Kenneth Russell's book *The Principles of Dairy Farming* by candlelight and having to be careful to blow out the candle before falling asleep! So here I was – the proud owner of ten heifers costing £50 each, and with great expectations.

The first two calved with only the minor disappointment that both calves were bulls. The going rate for a bull calf in those days was two shillings and six pence (25p). Wow! A heifer calf would have been about £3. This is because the bulls would go to be killed, as it is not profitable to rear a milk cow's calf for beef, but a female calf (heifer) would become a milk producer in the herd. This was what I wanted, to get my milking numbers up, as I was now a milk producer. At this time, my milking shed had not yet been passed by the Ministry, so my two heifers were being milked at Corn Hill Cop, Leominster, along with Mr. Rogers' milk herd. There was a delay with my new set-up as I had elected to be a TT producer, that is, a Tubercular Tested herd. It was just at this time, 1951, that a new test was carried out to make sure that cows did not carry the Tuberculosis disease. It was a wonderful thing and the start of the eradication of TB in humans. It is only now, some 50 years later, that TB is becoming a concern again. To get TT status, the premises had to be of a high standard and the water also had to be tested and approved. In addition, the cattle were tested annually. I can remember that at this time there was a big debate on whether badgers passed TB (which we knew that they carried) to human beings through contact with milk cows. A hue and cry was made when many badgers were culled in the West Country. It's a big disappointment that now, 50-odd years later, the whole procedure is being gone through again, with no progress made.

In 1948, whilst I was a shepherd in Kettlewell in the Yorkshire Dales, we had had a huge snow and many sheep had been lost. It was because of this that I had lost my job as moor shepherd. It was devastating for me and I was full of sorrow at having to leave my wonderful job, but I was now to find out what it had been like for my boss at that time, Mr. Middlemiss, to suffer a possible bankruptcy.

My next heifer due to calve looked great – fit and well, coat shining, dew drops on her nose – a picture of health. She settled down to calve and I sat and watched her. Her water bag burst – a sign that birth was imminent. I waited to help if it was needed; it is always better if the birth is unaided with no fuss – I often find pulling and twisting only aggravates everything and I am always loath to interfere. But an hour later, I was getting worried, as a calf can drown once the water bag has burst if he has not got his head out. His head was still in the womb and my heifer was very uncomfortable. I was not too worried as I could feel that his nose and feet were in just the right position – that is, front legs straight out and nose and head between them. Perfect. But she had been like this too long, so I called Mr. Rogers' cowman for his opinion.

He came and took a look, and said, "Give her time, she is ok." But after being told that she had been like this for over an hour, he said, "Ok, let's give her a helping hand."

Two ropes were secured, one to each front foot. Gallons of warm water and much soap were applied to give a smooth passage and we gently began to pull the ropes. No response – the calf was stuck fast. One hour later (it seemed like a week), we were no further forward. The cowman had not seen a birth like this with absolutely no progress at all in this length of time. It was past the time that the vet should have been called.

I went and called him with heavy heart, as I knew that a bill for £10 was coming with him. It's a terrible thing to think about money at such a time, but I did not have the funds. I started to explain to Mr. Blanchard (the vet) that money was a problem, but he would not listen, and ten minutes later he was with us. It did not take him long to tell us that we had got a "bulldog calf". Well, I had never heard of that. He explained that this condition was rare and is usually caused by a genetic fault in the bull which put the cow in calf. The calf is not disfigured in any way except for-up nose (hence the term bulldog) but is full of water and usually weighs about two-and-a-half cwt. (250 lb) instead of about 100 lb. It is alive up to the point of birth but dies immediately. It cannot be born naturally so the cow would have to have a caesarean birth – that is, through a cut in the side of the cow – so we had to get on with it before we lost the cow. Twenty minutes later, the calf was delivered – DEAD. Three of us had a job to lift it. It is the most sorrowful sight that I have ever seen – full of liquid contained in small compartments, just like an orange, that oozes out when you try to lift it – it's a tragedy.

The heifer was now stitched up and propped up on a bale of straw, exhausted. I feared for her life. She had had good drink of water (always a good sign); she would live, although I did not know it at the time. There is usually a silver lining and I was now to learn what a fine bunch of people these vets are. I was told that his bill would be £5, and I was not to worry and to give him a bit when I could. I was very relieved and learned a lesson to explain BEFORE asking for a service and not waiting until you get the bill before asking for time to pay. In my case, I would have had a bill for £10. Now I was grateful to get a bill for £5.

So, my first setback. I now realised it's not all "trouble free" being a farmer. I began to worry about my other seven in-calf heifers. With good reason – my next two heifers had bulldog calves. As I write this, I can once again feel the deep despair that I felt at the time. If this disaster had been of my own making I could have called myself a fool – an idiot – but I had not put a foot wrong – I had bought in good faith, no one could know that an inherited fault was there, but I still felt as if it was my fault. Then a thought struck me – the man who had sold me the heifers should be told, at once, so that he could stop using the bull. He would know which one it would be. I immediately got on my bike and shot off to the telephone and gave him a ring. Five minutes later, I was back in the farmhouse – I was in the most dreadful state. Myfanwy was on the receiving end of a most awful tirade – I said things to her that I am most ashamed of, even today. Finally, I was able to tell her that the man had known that the bull was throwing bulldog calves – that was why he'd sold the heifers. I made a promise to myself that if ever I knew something was wrong with any of my stock (livestock or deadstock, i.e. machinery) I would never pass it on without declaring it. Well, it's a good job I only had a bike and a lot of work to do, or murder might have been committed.

Five heifers still to calve; Myfanwy said, "Bad start ~ good finish", and, indeed, the next two calved well, and also, a bonus, two heifer calves – our first two. These would calve in two-and-a-half years' time to be our first home-grown milkers. The dread came back with the next calf – another bulldog, but once again we were able to save the cow, so we now had four cows that were not producing milk, but all were at least alive, and one still to calve. She was to calve all right, but we lost a big bull calf. We felt that we were lucky.

We now had to try and survive this bad start. It's a strange thing, but we never once thought of giving up. I knew that I could easily milk six cows and do a full day's work for some other farmer to get some money coming in, and that is what we did. Myfanwy was a tower of strength, never once complaining, never one word against the seller of the heifers, always there when money became a rare commodity with "it will come right".

And so started our life as farmers. It was about a month after our last heifer calved that a strange thing happened. I got up one morning to milk and walked the six cows into the cowshed, having previously put some hay in the mangers, when I noticed that there were seven cows (you can see how quick I am at 5 a.m.). The cow was a perfect match to mine, although it was a year older (more teeth up) and she was in milk (had had a calf recently), so I milked her along with mine. I would find out who her owner was later. But I didn't – no one claimed her. It was Myfanwy who suggested that the seller of our original ten heifers must have wanted to salve his conscience by dropping off this extra beast. When no one claimed her, I rang up the said seller, but he claimed he knew nothing about it. So I thanked him anyway and hung up. The police told me some time later that they no longer had any interest in her and she was now mine as far as they were concerned. I now like to think Myfanwy got it right. It also made her name complete as I had named our herd Molly, Yvonne, Freda, Alice, Nancy and Wendy, and now we had Yan.

The next problem was what to do about the four cows that had had bulldog calves. Should we put them in calf or not? The vet said that there was a query as to whether they would get in calf again owing to the mauling that they had taken at the last births, but if they "took to the bull" there was no reason to expect bulldog calves again – in fact, it was most unlikely. So we thought, right, let's see if they get in calf; if they do conceive we will keep them, if not, then they would be sold as barren cows for killing. They would definitely NOT be sold as breeding stock!

WHEN MYFANWY AND I got married in Ludlow on May 7th, 1951, we had some wonderful presents. Amongst them was a young gilt (female pig that has not yet had a litter), a present from Mr. and Mrs. Downing of Moss Hill Farm, Monkland, my first boss since coming down from Yorkshire. So now I could start a pig herd! Pigs should have five litters every two years, with about seven or eight piglets to each litter, so we should have a nice herd ere too long. Not only that, but to have our own bacon and ham would be really a fine bonus. I told you that I had been lucky with my bosses and this was a great present from one of them. Well, we called her "Joey". Looking back, it seems a bit disrespectful to Joe Downing, but this was not so at all. I thought the world of Mr. and Mrs. Downing. It was just the sort of daft thing that we did. Myfanwy's first dog – a golden Labrador – was called Basil and it was a bitch?? So "Joey" was walked up to a neighbour's boar and first time became "in pig".

She was bedded down in deep wheat straw and was really spoilt. She was well fed (scientifically, of course), so it was quite a surprise when she broke out of her pen one night. She only broke into the fold yard, and all would have been well except that we had just started making cider! I got up to do the milking and was greeted by a drunken pig! She had managed to push over a barrel of fresh-pressed apple juice – fortunately only a few gallons had run out, but it was enough to make her incapable of anything except rolling about and grunting. She was a real pain because I wanted to get on and milk or I would miss the milk lorry at seven-thirty, and she wanted to join me and the cows in the cow shed. Every time I went with a pail of milk to the dairy, there she was in the way. Later in the morning, it took the three men that were with the mobile cider press and myself to get her back into her pen.

I was pleased when she came to have her litter – we had seven good strong piglets. We were happy with that for a first litter, but would expect more in her next few litters. We really did not want a pig herd, just the one was enough, so all the litter were castrated, gilts as well as boars, and they would all go for bacon, one being kept for our own consumption and the rest off to Hereford market as weaners (i.e. sold off the sow at eight weeks). Although the majority of smallholders (farms up to about 50 acres – 20 hectares) were what we call mixed, it would have been too much to have taken the piglets from six weeks to bacon weight (10 score or 200 lbs), which takes about four months. At Buckfield we had dairy cows and two beef calves to try and take to killing weight at about three years. We never managed this, as some time before they were anywhere near "finished beef" we had to sell them to pay bills that seemed to come from an inexhaustible source – so we would start again with a couple of calves. The fold yard always had two or three dozen laying hens. Mixed in with those were guinea fowl of widely varying numbers depending on the time of year. The one thing that I surely missed were my dogs and sheep. Maybe some time in the future… but first we had to get established as farmers.

We had begun to get established when, in August 1952, a world-shattering event took place – our first son, John, was born. Myfanwy was thirty-one at the time and she had a difficult time. John was born in Leominster but Myfanwy had to go to Hereford to be looked after for a short while. And how I missed her.

She was the next to youngest of a family of nine, but her younger brother, David, had been killed in the war. It's a pity that all people are not farmers because then they would not have any time to spend fighting. (Get off your soap box, Robinson!) With all relations so close, I was well looked-after, and was able to get to Hereford because I had bought a car (well, a van – a Jowett). It had a two-cylinder engine, which sometimes dropped down to one! But it got me to Hereford until the great day arrived when mother and son were back at Buckfield. I remember that day well – it was a warm autumn day and no work got done – my brother-in-law Ralph from Corn Hill Cop came and milked for me. A GREAT DAY.

I cannot let this time pass without talking about an incident that took place a few days later. Dad came down from Yorkshire and brought with him a seven-year-old girl – the daughter of Mum and Dad's best friends. She had come to see Myfanwy… and the new baby. It was a surprise for us as we did not know they were coming and in those days it took four and a half hours for the journey. I happened to be up in the bedroom when the knock on the door came and I looked out of the bedroom window to see Dad and this little girl asking to see Mum and new baby. We'll meet the little girl, Helen, again later.

Buckfield Farm was half grass and half orchard. The orchard was a mixed blessing as the grass was always coarse and for quite a time could not be grazed. When the fruit was being harvested the cows could not be allowed in as we picked into sacks after shaking the apples onto the ground with what's called a 'panking pole'. This is a pole 10 or 11 feet long with a hook on the end to hook over a branch, which is then shaken to make all the fruit fall. A horse and cart or, later, a tractor and trailer were then driven around to pick up the bags and take them to the roadside to be loaded onto a lorry and off to Bulmers or Westons to be made into cider. Most of our trees were cider apples but we had quite a few Bramleys, Newton Wonder and Worcester Pearmain (i.e. cookers, cookers or eaters, and eating), but it was not often that we got a sale for these so they were shaken and picked and also went to the cider factory as "pot fruit", which went to make an apple juice drink. This fruit would sometimes pay for the rent of the farm but sometimes it was not possible to sell it at all. So it was a mixed blessing.

The times when there was no sale for the apples were a real pain as the cattle could not be allowed into the orchard as (1) they could choke on the apples, (2) even if they did not choke they might only eat a very few apples and get ill or (3) they got very loose – nasty.

As noted earlier, we used to make cider. There was a mobile cider mill that used to come round and pulp the apples and press them in what were called "cheeses". These were envelopes of a hessian-type material full of pulped apple then placed one on top of another in a press. When the press was stacked to the top, a screw was turned on top and a plate pressed down on the cheeses and tightened until all the juice was pressed out and collected at the bottom in a large tun dish. This was then poured into forty-gallon barrels and fermented into cider. This home-made cider (with certain secret additives) was essential on most small farms. I used to make two barrels every year. I never drank any as it was pure dynamite! But if you did not have any cider it was impossible to get any casual labour at hay-making or apple-picking time, for example, as it was expected as a free drink for the workmen. Being near to Leominster, we always had a few "gentlemen of the road" calling at the farm. We had our regulars who would appear out of the barn in the morning after sleeping off a pint or two of our cider – they would have a cup of tea and a bacon sandwich then set off on to their next port of call. They were never any trouble; they were always polite, though they smelt like a polecat!

Dad had been a very good sportsman – a cricketer, to be exact. He was a professional when he was seventeen, playing for Undercliffe in the Bradford League with George Gunn, and, as far as I know, he still holds the record for the fastest century in the Huddersfield League – forty-one minutes, with Ron Aspinall bowling at one end and Eddie Leadbeater at the other. Both these bowlers went on to play for Yorkshire.

I had not played much sport since my school days where I played rugby league, getting to play for the Huddersfield Under 15 team. We used to play in what was called a "curtain raiser" before the senior team game. I had enjoyed these games but on starting work I had not played again, that is, until I came down to Herefordshire where Mr. Downing (my first boss in Herefordshire) got me to play for the Luctonians (his old school). This was in 1948. At that time, the Luctonians had one team! We used to play in a field by the church and get changed in the Angel pub in Kingsland. The Luctonians today have many teams: 1st, 2nd, 3rd, 4th XV, plus many junior teams. I think there are five full-size pitches, three of them floodlit. It is a huge organisation and grown from just that one team in 1948. What a credit to the various committees.

I suppose that Dad being a very enthusiastic cricketer would have some effect on me at some stage. I always enjoyed a game of cricket on the common at Monkland on a Sunday. These were very rare but always good fun. It is amazing that there is so much talent in these local teams where the coaching is non-existent. I have seen sixes hit with the grace of a county player – not just "slogging". These games must have stirred something in me, as when asked if I would play for Leominster Wed XI, I said I would like the odd game. Myfanwy was pleased that I was having a break from work, and indeed I do believe that I could work better after a complete change.

I shall never forget my first game for two reasons. The first was that in the home team's changing room at the Grange there was an old score sheet framed on the wall. It was of a game played before the First World War, and the Leominster team displayed were all out for one run – and that was a bye! But the interesting thing was that the team was the Leominster Break of Day XI, who used to play before going to work in the morning! I often wonder if it was still dark when this team amassed a total of one.

The second thing was the beauty of the Grange – the whole setting was just wonderful. This first game was against a touring team from Manchester called the Old Bedonians. The players were all Fathers – the religious kind – so I think it must have been a Catholic school. During the game, there was much banter, with Father this or Father that getting quite a "ragging". They really did enjoy their cricket. It was when they were batting that they became a bit subdued as wickets fell a bit quickly. But, as is often the case, a lower-order batsman came in and set about our bowling. He scored an entertaining 50 before getting out. We were all together, after getting changed, and the usual "post mortem" had started, when I commented that Father John had played really well for his 50, and was surprised when the whole team erupted into gusts of laughter. No, said their captain – he's the bus driver!

AFTER BUYING THOSE ten heifers in late 1950 I had to get some form of bank account. I had no experience of this as I only had my Post Office deposit account, which was now empty but for a very small amount. My ex-boss Mr. Rogers said that he would take me to Lloyds Bank in Leominster and get me set up. An appointment was made with the manager and duly kept, at which I was asked, how much did I want to deposit? – Deposit, no, I wanted to have an overdraft. – Alright, what collateral did I have? – Collateral, what's that? – Guarantee – Oh, ten heifers. Bank manager: "But they are cows" – "Yes" – "Then they are not acceptable as a guarantee." – "Why?"

– "Because they are livestock and are likely to die." – "Likely
to die? I hope not." – "Hope is not enough, Mr. Robinson"
(note I am now Mr. Robinson) – "Well, what about hard work
and determination? And my name is Trevor." – "Nothing solid
there, Mr. Robinson." – "So you want me to have £100 before
you will lend me £100?" – "NO, Mr. Robinson, we want you
to have £200 before we lend you £100." – "Mr. Bank Manager,
if I had £200 I would not need your £100." – "Quite, Mr.
Robinson. Perhaps we should meet again when you are able to
give me some col-er-guarantee."

On getting back to Buckfield Farm, I took myself to my
'office' (i.e. the kitchen table) and seriously set about thinking
money. Throughout my working life, money had always been
tight and saving it was difficult, but I could usually put at least
a few shillings away. But now it was different; money had to be
managed to actually meet deadlines. For example, last month's
cattle feed had to be paid for before next month's could be
bought – the feed company just would not send your order if
you were not up to date with your account. That was alright
because, with milk, your milk cheque would come at the same
time as your feed bill was due. This is why I, a shepherd, was
producing milk – there should be enough money left over

for us to live on after paying the feed bill. In the case of a sheep farmer, ewes are put to the ram in October – they lamb in March and it's July before the lambs are sold. So there is no income for ten months, when the first income from the lambs is boosted by the wool cheque as the ewes are shorn in June. There is then enough money to pay not only the feed companies and living expenses but also the rent. A bad winter like 1948 and you are in trouble, because it's going to be another year before you have any more money coming in. So you can see that management has to be good not just to get as many ewes in lamb as possible but also to save as many lambs as possible at lambing time. Then you have to hope that the price at selling time is good. I suppose that's why shepherds are portrayed as quite philosophical (what a big word for me) and also why bank managers are so careful. It's even worse for the beef producer. A cow is put in calf and it's nine months before the calf is born – now there's the first gamble – we are hoping for a bull calf – 50% will be heifers.

Let's say we get a bull calf. At the time of my story, a bull calf took three years to attain maturity, so there was no income from that cow for three years and nine months, by which time, of course, there were another three offspring on the way, so it's four years before money becomes a yearly cycle. A long time and many things can go wrong, and also the beef farmer has absolutely no idea what price beef will be in four years' time! Once again, quite a gamble.

You will be able to see that it's pretty impossible to progress straight from being a farm worker to being either a sheep or beef farmer. If Dad is already a beef or sheep farmer and the cycle is up and running, it's no problem and such farmers' sons are at a great advantage.

Meanwhile, back at the kitchen table, many schemes were being thought of and much tea was being drunk. For example, let's start keeping – rabbits. They are quick breeders – saleable – not too expensive to buy – make a note to find the cost of making hutches and if it would be possible to find a market for the pelts (skins). The whole thing does not seem to fire me with enthusiasm. As I believe that this is a vital ingredient – pass. On to the next idea.

What about batteries? No, not things that start cars or go in torches – hen batteries. It's a new way to keep laying hens. Cages about two feet long and eighteen inches wide holding about five birds, in stacks of three high and back to back. All "mod cons", water laid on – feed in a trough all day long – sloping wire floor that rolls the eggs (dozens of them) into a tray in front. Just walk along and collect them. Sounds good. To me it sounds dreadful. I am an extensive farmer, definitely not an intensive one. Besides, hen muck is most revolting (I did not realise that I was a snob).

Well, if not hens, what about ducks? I do know that there is a local hotel that will buy fifty a month. Myfanwy likes the idea of ducks (we are therefore halfway there). Cost – one brooder – we have a barn that would be just right. I work out that profit would be about 2 shillings and sixpence per duck at eight weeks. Deaths about 4% – that leaves £8 or £1 per week. Myfanwy, you have got yourself a job. One thing I have not told Myfanwy, yet – ducks are great to train sheepdogs on.

About a week after my visit to the bank, I received a letter from the manager inviting me to see him on Thursday morning, if possible, at 10.30 a.m.

This set me off on a frantic chase trying to find a guarantor. At my first interview, the manager had suggested that maybe my parents should be consulted. I had declined to follow this up and it was not mentioned again. From an early age of 7 or 8, the only interest to me was farming. One of my uncles had a smallholding on Lindley Moor run in conjunction with a public house called the Friendly Inn (it's now under the M62). One of the first photographs I have is me sat on one of his pigs, age 7; so I suppose Uncle Frank was the cause of my choice of career.

I can remember very exciting days at the Friendly Inn.
They were called Hat days! They were, in fact, pigeon-shooting
competitions. Pigeons were placed on the ground, a top hat
put over them with a long string that reached over a stone wall
from where a man pulled it to release the bird – whereupon
the shooter tried to shoot the bird. The guns were old muzzle
loaders and great plumes of smoke and loud bangs were
emitted and usually the pigeons flew away. I now think the
idea is awful, but to a boy of seven, the bangs and smoke were
exciting.

Mum and Dad had been pleased that I knew just what I
wanted to do and had been very supportive but they had no
capital and small savings. There was no way that I was going
to jeopardise their small savings. I was on my own and I liked
it that way. So, having got no further, I went to the bank and
Mr. Robinson was shown in to see the manager. Bombshell –
Mr. Rogers had written to the bank to say he would guarantee
me for £200. Papers were here to sign and interest would be
7%. You are a very lucky man, Mr. Robinson. It was quite
some time before I could speak – I did not know what to say. It
was explained that Mr. Rogers would not have anything to pay
unless I failed to meet the bank's charges. His only loss would
be if I failed. This kept running through my mind – if I failed.
Up to this point, I had never, ever, thought of failure. The
thought of someone else losing if I failed did not seem right.
I could not do it, I could not sign the papers – if Mr. Rogers
could trust me why not the bank? I left the bank in a whirl –
papers not signed. I went down to Broadward Hall to see Mr.
Rogers and thank him for what he had done. His response was
that I would not let him down and so I should go back and
sign the papers. Slap on the back – shake hands – finish. But
I could not.

A week later, a letter from the bank – could I go and see
the manager next Thursday if possible at 10.30 a.m. and would
I take the enclosed form with me duly completed. Hello –

what's this? It's a form which is a statement of all my debts and all my assets. It does not take me long to fill in as I have not much of either! If I value my cows at £65 each my position looks quite healthy. The trouble is, as always, cash or, as it is known today, cash flow, having enough capital to buy before I sell, not after the sale.

Off I go to the bank on Thursday. I am shown into see the manager. "Nice to see you, Mr. Robinson, have you thought any more about your overdraft?" – "No, I have not got one." He studies my statement – grunts – "I think you have valued your stock a bit high, Mr. Robinson. I would have thought £50 per cow about right! Mr. Robinson, I can offer you an overdraft of £100 at 10% interest. I shall require you to fill in one of these statements every three months when I visit your farm to collect it. Does my offer interest you, Mr. Robinson?" – "Yes, it does thank you very much." I stand up and shake his hand. Business over, I turn to go, then – another surprise – "Good luck, Trevor, I know you will not let me down."(!) I was lucky as in those days a bank manager had the authority to grant things without referring to the head office.

Things were now moving very fast in agriculture. Even a smallholding like mine was greatly affected. Cowsheds with cows lying on deep straw were being replaced by milking parlours and silage was slowly taking over from hay, which in turn brought the two evils of slurry and silage effluent together – and, coupled with having to milk with the parlour doors open, this brought problems that have not been solved, even after about 50 years. The cubicles that cows are now made to lie in seem to give problems for feet and hocks, while getting rid of the slurry is a major problem. Life is not as good for man nor beast as when deep straw yards and cowsheds were the norm. I said earlier that progress sometimes gallops in the wrong direction; even if profit is better, animal welfare is not.

Great steps have gone into the science of feeding. When cow cake was first made, 8 lb. of cake could produce a gallon of milk. By getting the correct balance of oil protein and carbohydrates, it was soon down to 6 lb. per gallon Then by getting the correct balance of animal to vegetable protein, it came down to 5 lb. per gallon. Then by doing the same with the carbohydrates, it got to 4 lb. per gallon. Then splitting the protein again to degradable and non-degradable got it down to 3½ lb. per gal. What a success story that is. I seem to have got ahead of myself here, as this progress took about thirty years, but that is still fast by any standard.

By contrast, when I started to milk in my cowshed I used to feed my home-grown cereals. About five acres would be ploughed and sown with dredge corn. That was a mixture of oats, wheat, barley, peas, vetches, and beans. This all grew up together and was cut with the binder, stooked, and hauled into the barn, then after about six weeks it was threshed. The idea was that by mixing the seed like this the resulting mix was a correct balance of protein and carbohydrates for milk production. So when it was ground up it could be fed in the manger without any additions. It was rocket science in those days but it was soon shown to be rather haphazard.

The Ministry of Agriculture, Fisheries and Food were the driving force behind these great strides in production at this time. There were many lectures on new techniques, so that every night could have been taken up by going to one of these. Things really were buzzing. It was the wish of the Ministry that every acre should produce its maximum – every animal should reach its full potential and every farmer should be an expert in his field. Food had been short during the war and they were making sure that in the future we achieved the maximum that we were able to. And indeed, things took off like a rocket. With the advent of fertilisers and chemicals, large companies like ICI, Fisons and Shell saw a big potential for advancement and profit. They were quick to put men in the field and exploit the situation. These men were clever and well qualified and were a tremendous help in explaining the techniques and pointing the way for a working farmer to go. I was young and keen to employ these new practices and joined up with ICI to obtain their services, which were free so long as you bought their product. The first ICI fieldsman that came round to my farm in the early 1950s is still a close friend today – even though he now lives in Canada, he comes over to "the old country" every year and stays with us. So the impetus started by the Ministry was boosted by these large companies, so farming really did get a kick up the backside.

One of the hazards of milking on a small farm on the outskirts of a town is that at some time the cows will have to walk along the main road which goes into town. Winter time was not too bad as the cows remained in the yard after milking, where it was just a case of calling them up in the morning and milking would soon be under way. The same applied in spring and summer when they were turned out into the fields adjacent to the farm. It was a different story when the fields further away had to be grazed. It was usually ok to bring the cows along the road between 5 a.m. and 6 a.m. but taking them back after milking was a different tale. These days were governed by the time that the milk lorry arrived to collect the milk churns. I was right on the boundary of Leominster. In fact, my milk stand was right next to the road sign that said "Leominster". As the driver lived in Leominster, I became his first pick-up at 8 a.m. So milking had to be finished, the cowshed cleaned out and swilled and the three or four churns had to have been pulled by hand on my four-wheeled milk cart down to the road for 8 a.m.. All good so far. I, like most dairy farmers, liked to get the cows back to the field as soon possible so that they could eat their fill and lie down to "make next milking's milk".

Well, no doubt you have worked out the time of day that my turn-out came to – Yes, 8.30 a.m., just the time that the workers were coming in to work. I saw two disadvantages in this: (1) the fact that these drivers were only just going to work when I had already done 2½–3 hours' work so I did not see that they should hassle me, (2) my cows were being pushed along at too fast a pace and any upset in routine always caused less milk at next milking (i.e. less income) and (3) (I used to be good at counting) I was ready for my breakfast so I was not in the right mood to be shouted at. Also, my cows were not at all bloody. Well, let me say at once, 99% of drivers were great but, of course, there's always one, ain't there? Unfortunately, my one went to work at the same time every day and I turned out at the same time every day. He was driving a black Ford 8 car. I knew it well. I had a lovely old cow called Camellia; she gave a lot of milk but she was a bit slow on her feet and was always at the back of the herd with me. For two or three days, I had been told by this driver to "shift the B____ thing out of his way", which I did, but obviously not fast enough, and he had got to the point of driving about 6" away from Camellia's back legs. This irked me – and I told him in no uncertain terms that if he touched her back leg I would put my not inconsiderable stick across the bonnet of his motorcar. This situation had gone on for about a minute when he did touch Camellia's back leg. I started to lift my stick but Camellia was quicker than me and with the speed of light she lashed out backwards. Now, these Ford 8s had a small sidelight perched on top of the mudguard and she hit one of these like a golfer hitting a golf ball and it shot 20 yards

down the road, clean as a whistle. Well, it's a long time since I laughed as much. It must have been an odd sight, I just could not stop laughing. I would have fallen over but my stick held me up. I looked at the driver and he just had to join in because by now two or three people were laughing at me laughing, if you see what I mean. At any rate, we both just roared. When I was at last able to speak I said I would pay for a new light, and from that day we were good friends – good old Camellia.

WHEN WE HAD first moved into Buckfield I had bought an old Fordson standard tractor. This was the tractor that was the accepted work horse and many farm carts and horse-drawn implements were pulled by it using an adaptation called an iron horse. This was simply a straight piece of angle iron that rested on the back piece connection shafts and hooked onto the drawbar of the tractor with a crosspiece of angle iron that held up the front end of the shafts. So this iron cross was where the horse should have been and now the tractor was in front of this. It was, of course, an adaptation and as such was soon outdated. At this time, a hydraulic engineer called Harry Ferguson came along and the Fergi was born. It was a complete system where the tractor and various implements were fastened together by hydraulic arms. When the arms were up, the implement was out of work and the handy little tractor was very manoeuvrable. The arms could put the implement at any working depth or be lowered so that the implement ran along the surface. It made it so easy to plough – work down – drill the seed and run a mower along the surface The only trouble was that to get the best out of the system, all this had to be bought as well, quite expensive but very good.

From my point of view, one of the best new implements, without a doubt, was the tractor-pulled string-tying hay baler. This really was a boon; the days of the pitchfork were numbered. In previous days, after the horse had turned and windrowed the hay (put two swaths into one), it was a case of hand pitching the windrow onto a cart, taking the load to the hayloft or unloading the loose hay and building it into a stack or pushing it into a loft. Then, of course, it had to be hand cut with a hay knife and carried loose to the cattle. A lot of hard work. There were hay sweeps of various kinds, but at some stage, the hay had to be man-handled, a tough and sweaty pressurised job. And it took time, so there was more chance of rain spoiling the hay. This new baler just went round and round the field collecting up the windrow with a tined reel, and out came lovely oblong bales at the back end. By tightening or slackening the outlet tube you could make the bales to whatever weight you wanted. The bales were then collected by cart and were handled by a short hay fork. The big pitchfork became a museum piece. This system, with a little modernisation, is still used today, but even in the 1950s, it was being superseded by silage. But that's another story.

Life at Buckfield was going well. John was growing up. I called him a "white-faced un" because he was born in the county of the white-faced Hereford cattle. He was a happy child (I had not yet started to knock him into shape) and Myfanwy and myself were very happy in our work. We were slowly getting over our bad start. The milk cows now numbered fifteen and, wonderfully, three out of our four "bulldog" heifers had a calf, only one having to go for meat. It could not have been a better outcome. The fifteen cows were on 32 acres of grass, and as half of the grass was orchard it was about as far as we could get. I was beginning to think that we would have to change to a 'flying herd'.

Right, well, this means that replacements for the herd are bought in and not bred, so that land taken up with the young stock can be used by milk cows as the young stock will go. As a stock farmer, it is usual to want to breed your own replacements, thereby establishing your own strain, which you are able to improve by using selected bulls exclusively. Over the years, as the herd reaches the maximum that the farm will carry, you will be able to sell your surplus stock at a premium. This is the position to aim for and it must be wonderful to attain it. My trouble was that I only had 32 acres and it was not enough to aspire to this end. So I had to try and maximise my milk gallonage. To do this, I would buy in cows that had just calved, milk them for one lactation then sell them when they went dry. They would, of course, have been put in calf after being in milk for about three months so the buyer of these now dry cows would have to wait about two to three months for them to calve. When I could possibly buy them back again! In putting them in calf I would use another new innovation called artificial insemination (often called the bull in the bowler hat!), so I would not need to keep a bull. So, you see, all my time would be taken by managing a milking herd. This could be taken a step further by buying in all my fodder, i.e. hay, so that the land required to make hay on could again be utilised for more milk cows. Although this system was not what I had envisaged when I came to Buckfield, it was a way I could use my small acreage to the full. Plenty to think about there.

Since getting my farm in September 1950 I had not had much time for anything other than getting established, with just the odd game of rugby and cricket and a few ploughing matches. During the time with Mr. Downing, I had made friends in all these things and one of them was called John Gwilliam; he was a champion ploughman. At that time, John worked for Mr. Sangers, who farmed between Eardisland and Pembridge. He was a big farmer and John would spend all week ploughing with a big crawler tractor pulling maybe four or five furrows – a big outfit – but at weekends he would swap this for his old standard Fordson pulling two furrows, and off he would go to a ploughing match. He happened to be a good friend of mine so that I could find out where he was ploughing the next week. I would then find somewhere else to go because I could never beat him. (No joke – Yes, honest). If John was ploughing out Leominster way he would often leave his plough at Buckfield, and when he came to collect it we would have a chat to get up to date with the latest techniques. He won the British Championship on several occasions and one time he went to Italy and won the World Championship. Yes, he was very, very good. Mind, he should have been because his dad, who was a close neighbour of mine, had been for many years the British Horse Plough Champion and was now a greatly respected ploughing judge.

Old Mr. Gwilliam was a farm worker for the farmer who farmed next door to Corn Hill Cop where I had once lived in as a farm worker. Corn Hill Cop was on top of a ridge and we could look down on where Mr. Gwilliam used to work. It was wonderful to see the everyday work that Mr. Gwilliam did. It did not matter whether it was ploughing, drilling or sowing mangolds or sugar beet – the work was just perfect. These wonderful patterns in different directions but all dead straight were a beautiful tapestry of ever-changing colours. I am sure the pleasure that we got from looking down on them was even better than they were close to.

Well, where was I? Yes – John's plough – after he had collected his plough and gone I would get the urge to have another go at match ploughing – I had my Fordson tractor but no plough, so on one occasion, off I went to Corn Hill Cop to see if my last old plough was there. It was, but in such a state – shall we say a bit sorry for itself. Well, I brought it down to Buckfield, stripped it down, cleaned, painted and replaced all the worn parts, then put it back together. It took a while in my spare time, but it looked ok. The next match happened to be the Leominster one – not much travelling there, so I thought, let's have a go as it's not far to trudge home if make a mess. I had not ploughed for a while, and in any case, John was in the open – I had to give myself some chance. But on looking at the ones ploughing – Goodwin, Philips, Samuels, Watkins – there was no weakness anywhere. Perhaps it was a bit cheeky, but I was now a farmer, even though only a little one, so I entered the class for farmers and farmers' sons. I took a lot of hammer when I turned up – Who's that? Is it the whiz kid from Ireland? Are they giving a prize for the best turned-out plough? – I think I recognise him. I've definitely seen that cap before. – So it went on.

I do not know what it was but I really enjoyed it. There seemed to be a lightness in the whole event. The ploughing just flowed – measurements were achieved without the usual tension. At one time, about halfway through, I actually caught myself looking across the whole field, whereas normally my eyes are glued to the furrows that are being drawn out. I think it was the weather. It was the first week in October but it was spring-like and the soil was moist – just right. The plough sliced through it with ease – sometimes it can be very dry and the plough "fumbles" through it – but not today. It was a big class. I cannot remember if there were nineteen and me or nineteen with me, but it was good to win it. For indeed I did. Going round the other plots with us all piled onto two tractors was good fun and I was able to inquire as to what those blue and yellow cards were for, and why did they insist on giving me a dull red one?? At this point, I was unceremoniously thrown off the tractor! So it was great to have started my match ploughing with a first prize and to finish my match ploughing with a first prize, for I was not to match plough again in Herefordshire. It had been an experience that I would not have liked to have missed. Wonderful men, farmers and farm workers.

It was decision time at Buckfield, do I go ahead and specialise in milk production? It's a way forward but I'd only be milking for the milk cheque – I am still a shepherd at heart, and I think that to go into something just for money must be wrong if your mind is hankering for something else. It's alright for a "stop-gap" measure to stabilise, but the sooner that you can revert to ambition, the better. Life is much more comfortable and is enjoyed much more. I have now got extra responsibility with not only Myfanwy but my son John to look after. I wonder what he would like to do? Heck, he is just turned one year old – maybe I should wait a bit before I ask him.

At times like this, some event often happens to help you make your mind up. Well, it certainly did for me. As recorded in a previous book, Mr. Tom Rogers, my boss, had given me the wonderful chance to get started on the farming ladder. It was an unbelievable thing to have happened, a chance that is only experienced by a very few, and I shall never forget the feeling of gratitude and wonder that I felt that day when I shook hands with this great man, when Buckfield Farm got me as a new – green – tenant. That was three years ago.

I can now let you into a little trade secret. Mr. Rogers was not only farming about six hundred acres but was also a well-known dealer in beef cattle. Before I came to Buckfield, Mr. Rogers used to use it as a place where he could put groups of cattle that he had bought. It was better for him not to have these temporary herds mixing with his own stock, so Buckfield was just right for this purpose. I should explain that Buckfield was on a ridge. A place with views that stretched from Clee Hill in Shropshire to the Black Mountain in Wales. A lovely place but, as my old boss Mr. Downing said, "you cannot farm a view, lad."

Well, this is Buckfield. It lies just outside Leominster between two roads which run along the full length, so whichever road you come off you go uphill to the house. This is important for my tale. There is not a much better sight than a herd of Hereford cattle with red and white markings lying in an emerald-green field. Just slightly less good is a field of Hereford bullocks about half-grown – I say slightly less because cows and calves add just that bit more variation. At any rate, this was the situation. Now, a buyer coming to Buckfield would not only have this lovely sight but in walking into the field off the road, the cattle would also be slightly above him! Well, so they look bigger, don't they? You must realise that I can only give you a little trade secret and belonging to someone else – I don't mind you knowing all mine. Since I had come to Buckfield, Mr. Rogers had once or twice asked if he could drop off a load of bullocks into one of my fields just for a day when he was stuck. So this day when he called I thought maybe I would be getting a load the next day. But no, could he have a cup of coffee? – Of course, come in and see Myfanwy and John. Now straight to the point, would I like to buy Buckfield? What a shock! Well, yes, of course I would. How much? £5000! A quick flash through my mind – Lloyds manager: "I don't think so, Mr. Robinson." I knew at once that I had no chance at all. There was no point in me spending time on a lost cause, as my total assets were not one fifth of that amount and no way could I have a loan of this size in any case. I did not/and indeed still do not know why Mr. Rogers wanted to sell, but I do know that there would have been a good reason.

So, what to do? I am a tenant. I pay rent; I have got rights under this agreement and so long as I pay my rent, I can just sit there and at some stage I will have a new landlord. So carry on and decide whether to have a "flying herd" or what? But situations are never as simple as they look. My problem was this – Mr. Rogers had given me a chance in a million, he, with Mr. Downing and Mat Middlemiss had given me a solid foundation – and given it to me, freely, most willingly, and sincerely, not only in my work but also in morals. My work for these extraordinary men was undertaken with me living in with them and their families. Now if I sat tight and waited for a new landlord I would be called a "sitting tenant", thereby showing the landlord-to-be that the farm was already let. This in turn made Buckfield worth quite a lot less than if it was sold "with vacant possession". In other words – empty. So there was no doubt that I would have to leave. I had nowhere to go. I had a wife and eighteen-month-old son. My life was turned upside down, so the sooner I got focused the better.

At this time, it was very hard to get a farm, because agriculture was in a healthy state and all produce was in demand. There were always good, well-known farmers' sons on the lookout for a farm of their own, so they were the first choice on any estate that their dads were on, and on any other estate, as far as that goes. So, apart from buying, it was difficult. I had some advantage through the fact that I was now a farmer myself, albeit a small one. Once I started looking, it became obvious that the real farming counties were out. Herefordshire, Shropshire, Worcestershire were impossible to break into, even with the backing that I was able to get. So my search had to be farther afield to the non-arable counties, or the poorer land in hillier counties. I don't know how many farms I went to look at, but many in Wales and one of these was in Carmarthenshire, and I got to the stage of being in the last two for the tenancy – myself and a professor from the University of Wales at Aberystwyth. I got really excited and looked forward to getting back into sheep, then I heard that they had given it to the professor. It hit me very hard and I began to lose hope.

Mum and Dad up in Yorkshire were also concerned – not for me, but for Myfanwy and John. Mum said Dad was hassling all his friends, who were mostly cricketers, but it made no difference, they had to help by thinking of some distant friend or acquaintance who might help. Cricketing friends in York, Scarborough, Barnsley, Sheffield, Settle were all asked; I believe Dad even asked cricketers in Giggleswick College and Worksop College to help. When we finally got a chance, it came from a most unexpected source. Dad had a sister – my Auntie Rene and her husband, Uncle Cyril, who worked as Quarry Manager at Otley for Stephen Toulson. Uncle Cyril was talking to Mr. Toulson one day and said that his brother-in-law was looking for a farm for his lad. Mr. Toulson said, "I have got two unoccupied at the moment. Tell him to send his son to see me"! Dad got in touch with Mr. Toulson and arranged an appointment for me to meet him at the farm. He was very sorry, but one of the farms had been let, so it was Springs Farm, Misson, or nothing. The farm was 169 acres and, as Dad said, as flat as a pancake. The buildings on it were very good but there was no water laid on or any electricity, apart from one light in the cowshed, which ran off a diesel generator – none in the house – obviously got the priorities right! Stephen Toulson were sand and gravel merchants so the

farm was very different from what I was used to. The rainfall for the area was an unbelievable twenty-one inches in a year – the lowest in the country – Leominster was double that. This should have registered more with me at this time, but it did not. 169 acres was very big after my 32 acres, and it was a strange thing, but it was exactly the same size as Moss Hill Farm, Monkland, Mr. Downing's farm. You will be able to imagine my excitement while on my way to Misson from Leominster.

Mr. Toulson was an out-and-out businessman. He wore a three-piece suit, was very brisk and I had to be "on my toes" to keep up with him. Any objection to what he said was instantly accepted or rejected with no argument. Terms were given to me – rent £5 per acre – water to be laid on as soon as possible – electric, same – ingoing owing to Mr. Fowler (the tenant who was leaving) to be paid to Mr. Toulson, who would settle with Mr. Fowler when depreciation had been assessed – tenancy from November 1953 – first rent to be paid up to March 1954 in advance. A draft agreement would be sent to me for my perusal – one week allowed prior to acceptance or refusal. Then – you will want to make arrangements with Mr. Fowler, so good afternoon and a very quick almost non-existent handshake. And he was gone – in his Rolls Royce. My head was spinning – whirlwind and gale-force wind came to mind. I stopped at Springs Farm to talk to Tom Fowler and find out why he was leaving. His answer was simple – the rent was going up to £5 and he did not think it was worth it. He had tried to point this out to Mr. Toulson but Mr. Toulson would not budge. It was take it or leave it. I said what about arbitration? Tom thought it would cost too much and he would probably lose, so he was going, There was no doubt in my mind that I would accept the tenancy and once more bite much more off than I could chew.

It was a big relief for us to know that we had somewhere to go. It was going to be a big wrench for us, especially for

Myfanwy. They were a big family and all lived in the Ludlow–Leominster area. She would be going 150 miles away, with only my Mum and Dad anywhere near, but she was very happy to go and in fact it was me who missed Leominster the most. Often during the first year at Springs Farm I would say one day we will go back, but Myfanwy said I don't want to, I am happy here – I thought what a lucky fellow I was.

Springs Farm

One last thing I did before going to Springs Farm was to buy a flock of thirty ewe lambs to take with us. I just could not wait until I got there. We moved the farm lock, stock and barrel to Springs Farm by rail. Looking back, I should have had a sale and started again. But I felt that I could cope better with the stock that had come this far with me. So they did, even Joey moved with a young litter of 10 piglets. Also to move with us was a young lad from Leominster called Eddie Freeman.

He had been coming to Buckfield as a schoolboy at weekends and he was a grand lad, so I asked him if he would like to come and live in with us on our new adventure. I was really chuffed when he said yes.

There was not much time to settle in as we had milked the cows at Buckfield in the morning and now they had to be milked at Springs Farm in the evening, Also, at Leominster we had milked in a cowshed and we now had a new milking parlour which the cows had never been in before. The pristine state of the parlour was soon to be well and truly christened! I had learned many years ago that stock must be handled quietly, and indeed this approach meant that by the following night's milking, the cows were walking into the new stalls as if they had been doing it all their lives. One trouble that we had was with the water. We were not yet on the mains and my TT status meant that the water from the well had to be tested. It was a surprise to me when the results of the test came through – the water was ok for us to drink but not good enough for the cows!? We were able to hold on to our TT status but mains water had to be installed ASAP. In the event, it was two years before this was done. And what a boon it was when we were able to get not only constant water but good pressure, as well.

Springs Farm was quite a handful for me in more than one way. The first thing was that it was five times bigger than Buckfield – this took some getting used to. The farm had been run by Mr. Fowler as an arable farm so the hedges had not been managed for the keeping of livestock; there was a tremendous amount of work to do there. As a stop-gap measure, miles of electric fence had been strung around various fields to keep the stock in. In the early days, TT licences were checked by the local police, who had to come and sign a livestock movement book which recorded the incoming and outgoing of all stock. One morning P.C. Don came to sign my book just as I was turning the cows out after milking, so I asked him if he would fasten the electric fence up on his way out. This entailed taking hold of a plastic handle and hooking it to a loop across the drive, which completed the circuit and made the fence live. To get the wire tight, there was a spring in the plastic handle, and to reach the loop this spring was under some pressure, so it was easy to do, it just needed a pull. I watched the P.C. stop his motorbike, pick up the handle and try to connect it up. The spring must have been stronger than he thought because it would not quite reach the loop. So, with his left hand he got hold of the bare wire to assist – well, he jumped a couple of feet in the air as he received the electric shock, threw the handle on the floor, got on his motorbike and left at great speed! At later dates he avoided coming when there was a wire across the drive!

There is a theory that to start farming, £100 per acre capital is required. When I started in 1950 I had £500, so I had the accepted capital for 5 acres! The requirement figure is worked out by agriculturists to cover the capital and running costs to get started. At Buckfield, I only had 32 acres so the difference between what I had and what I really needed was about £2,500. A big figure in those days, but providing I was careful, it would be possible, but difficult, to manage. I was now in a very different situation – estimated requirement: £17,000 – capital I had: £1,500. I had done well to get my capital to three times my starting figure, but I was still woefully short. This figure of £100 per acre was arrived at by adding up the cost of seed, fertiliser, a share of machinery costs, rent and living for a year. It would mean that all these things would be bought and paid for with a safety margin built in for unexpected costs. I don't think that many farmers had this luxury, nor expected it, but my capital was just ridiculous. I really did not have a chance. If I had realised this at the time I would not have taken on the tenancy, so what a good thing youth and naivety is.

Friends and relations were now miles away and we were on our own. New friends had yet to be made; the first in the business world had to be, yes, the bank manager, and I went in to Doncaster Lloyds Bank to what was the first of many, many meetings. I have got to say that without the early help of Bill Rowlands, the manager, I would have been lost. His help and understanding through many difficult times enabled me to survive. I am sorry to say that the freedom that was given to me would not be tolerated today; Bill Rowlands made decisions that are not now allowed without the authority of the Head Office – these are the men with no faces and no soul and who are certainly not capable of "instinct" or "vision", or even the notion of "giving a chance" to a young man, no matter what the man on the spot had to say. I think that this is a big mistake today, as by giving me a chance, the bank were to profit by a huge amount (I often say that one of Lloyds Bank's branches is owned by me because I've paid for it!). The loans and overdrafts given to me were only thinly covered by collateral guarantees; therefore, the interest was usually 3% above the bank's normal rate. I remember one time when I gained a loan at 10% it had risen to 21% within five months, nothing to do with me, just the state of other outside influences – believe me, it was crippling. This sort of pressure had a great effect on the ability to work – when your mind is trying to make ends meet, work suffers just when extra effort is needed.

So a plan is required. Part of the land would have to be let to another farmer until I could manage to acquire enough capital to farm it. That's easy, neighbours were always looking for land to grow potatoes on. Mr. Fowler had grown them successfully here so there would be plenty of takers. I would like to have grown potatoes myself, but the costs were far too high, with fertilisers, seed and chemicals adding up to £500 per acre, and then machinery and labour for picking, coupled with at least eight months waiting for a return – it was out of my reach.

So let's see what we can do. We have the cows, let's get them up to twenty – they will require about 60 acres for grazing and hay (silage?). We can grow our own cereals and protein – that is, peas or beans. The sheep can follow the cows and clean up the grass fields but will need 20 acres of their own for hay and management, i.e. land required when weaning-off the lambs. So land required for stock – let's say 90 acres. Much of the capital to do this could be supplied by subletting for the potatoes. As rent for potato land was about £20 per acre, £5 of this I would have to pay to my landlord, so if I let 30 acres I would have £450 to help with the livestock. We are left with 50 acres which can be sown with cereals. I could now go to a local merchant and arrange to buy seed, fertilisers and chemicals to plant this acreage. Built into this deal would be a "pay at harvest" agreement. This meant that the merchant would not get paid until I sold the grain. I would only be able to sell my harvest to this merchant so I had to have confidence in him as well as him trusting me. It would, of course, cost me quite a bit in interest charges, and I was in a weak position to drive for a good price when at the same time asking for long-term, unsecured, credit. This merchant credit is taken by most working farmers; it's only a few that are lucky enough to manage without it.

So that was the plan. Quite simple, but as I am no high-powered businessman, it had to be. Well, even this simple plan went wrong in a big way. I had arranged with a neighbouring farmer for him to grow potatoes on my land and he had ploughed the first 12 acres when I got a letter from my landlord saying "Please read your tenancy agreement, you will see that you are not allowed to sublet." Lesson No. 1: don't assume what you sign but read it, and if you don't understand it – ask. Now, if I had been more experienced I could have avoided this situation by going into partnership with the grower and sharing the profit at the end. I will not take this theory any further because I had stated that I was subletting so I had missed the chance. It was too late. The outcome was that my big plan was now in tatters.

When things go wrong it usually happens at a bad time, and this happened with me. I went off to the bank to try and arrange yet more credit – i.e. raise my overdraft – only to find that Mr. Rowlands had gone off on a course and would not be back for three months. So we had a temporary manager in. I had been to the bank on many occasions and had got to know the bank manager's secretary very well. She was great and had often forewarned me as to the health and temper of the manager at the time. So, it was "Good morning, Jane. How's the land lie this morning?" I knew that the manager was a small man who stood up very straight and tried to bolster his authority by "barking" at people. I never found that this approach was the right one to get the best out of people, and this morning, Jane (not her real name) was to emphasise this. Her reply to my question was, "Well, Trevor, if he speaks to me like that again, I will pick him up and sit him on top of the filing cabinet, and NOT lift him down again". I was in for a rough time! I had to wait for Mr. Rowlands to get back before progress was made. Having been told that I would not have got what I already had if he (the temporary manager) had been in charge (the man had no soul), I went back to my chosen seed and grain merchant and increased my order (which in turn increased my credit), so this was now in order. I was now beginning to collect debts and extended credit at a great rate. Many people were helping me but the responsibility was getting a bit much. I had the landlord (rent), the seed merchant, the cow feed firm, and the ever-present bank manager, who were all trusting me to succeed and I was just about to add one more, a machinery firm.

I thought long and hard about this – my motto had always been "think what you can do without, not what you can do with". So it was with a little feeling of apprehension that I added the machinery firm to my list. It was imperative that I got my harvest of grain in quick time, and at the right time to get the best return that I could. The farm was very light land – sand and gravel – so we could not grow wheat as this grows best on heavy clay land. So we grew oats and barley – the barley was ok as regards ripening because the ripe grains are firmly fastened to the head so can wait a while without deteriorating or falling off. Oats were a very different proposition, since when ripe the oats would fall off very quickly. Not only that, but if we had just one day of wind when the crop was ripe, one third of the oats would be on the floor and wasted, so they must be harvested as soon as possible. So, although there were contractors in the area, you would be lucky to get one just when you required one. As harvest time only lasts about six weeks, you can see that I was anxious. This brings home the problem about most agricultural machines – the baler – combine – seed drill – sprayer – hay turner – silorator (for making silage) and mowing machine are all only used for a short time of the year – most of their "lives" are spent sitting doing nothing in the implement shed. Only the tractor and trailer are used most of the year. It is so easy to tie up money in buying machines that it's better to use contractors, if possible. So you can see the contractors are very busy at these important times and they will work for the large farmers if possible, as this means being able to travel less and work more acres in the short time of these various operations. This in turn meant I would be one of the last in line, not only because of my "small" acreage but also because they would have to wait until I had sold my grain before I could pay them.

Farming at this time was in good heart. There were many small farms that were able to buy good second-hand machinery that was being replaced regularly by larger farmers, so it was possible to buy a machine when it was in the middle of its storage time. So, with the utmost urgency required by my harvest, I bought an old second-hand combine in the middle of winter! When I first approached the machinery firm, I was referred to the boss, as I was not known by any of his other customers so I did not have a reference, so to speak. On looking back, I now find it interesting that the boss said that he was very busy at the moment but he would be "in my area" tomorrow and could call round if convenient. The following day he came round and met Myfanwy and John and, over a cup, asked many searching questions. I really felt drained when he left. Despite him finding out how deep in debt I was, he was able to find me a really first-class combine at a fantastic price. Once again, I had managed, by sheer good luck, to pick a machinery firm with such a wonderful owner.

In writing about these various machines, and the costs involved, it brings to mind the amount of skill and responsibility of the farm worker. Machines like the combine and baler are complicated and the knowledge of the farm worker using them has to be vast. If a blockage or breakdown occurs he must be able to fix it, because time is of the essence; also mechanics are flat out at these times and it may be a couple of days before it's your turn to have one. So time saved by your own men is very important. So not only do they have to have the skill to use these machines to the maximum but they also need the knowledge to keep them running. At other times, he will also maybe have to be a stockman as well, and again, lay a hedge or build a stone wall. I cannot give enough praise to these stalwarts and am pleased to say that their skill is acknowledged by the farmers employing them.

It was while using my combine that my next disaster happened. I was working too late at night, the dew had come down so the grain was not flowing as well as it should, and, of course, an elevator was unable to cope and bunged up – belts started to slip and soon I was well and truly stopped. The works of the combine are run off the same engine that propels it, by a series of belts. I was able to stop the forward motion of the combine in the usual way, by putting the gear lever in neutral, but the engine was still running. The works of the combine are put into gear simply by pressing a jockey pulley onto a belt that connects the engine to the works. When enough pressure is applied, the belt is tightened and the works then turn. When this pulley is taken off the belt, the works stop and the belt – now being too big – just hangs on the works' side pulley – loosely over the engine pulley while it is still going round at speed. I should have stopped the engine, but at least the works were out of gear. I set about clearing the bunged-up elevators and got them clear. I just had one now blocked at the bottom in the combine, very awkward to get at, but I got in and just as I got the last obstruction out, to my horror, the combine began to work. The worm elevator grabbed my hand and wound me slowly into the combine until my body once again made the pulley slip. To this day, I do not know why or how the machine started to work, as the jockey pulley was not applied, or at least not fully applied. I know that I had cleared the blockage so the workings would now work easily, but they should not have done without the jockey pulley full in place. Now, to be honest, I do not remember the next two hours that it took to get me out, I just remember being unable to move, with my hand stuck and also my foot stuck. The top of the combine had to be cut away to release me. The firemen must have had quite a hectic time, and I shall forever be grateful to them and also to my doctor, who was with me for over one and a half hours before I was taken to hospital. Lesson No. 2: always switch off an engine before working on it!

During the next two years, I had five operations and was restored into good working order by two most wonderful men. First at Doncaster by Mr. Sinclair then at Harlow Wood, Mansfield by Mr. Pulvertaft from Derby. What a debt I owe them. Two funny things happened – the first at Doncaster, a few days after first going in, a nurse came to fetch me to change the dressing on my hand. I was taken into a small cubicle at the end of the ward. I had to carry a bottle of some liquid which was connected to me by a tube and hold it up whilst she undid my dressing. The nurse was really giving me a good talking to and telling me what a fool I had been when the last dressing came off – OK – she said and passed out cold on the floor!

The second was at Harlow Wood. I was getting better and was pretty fed up with being in hospital. Harlow Wood was in a lovely location on a hill in a wood, of course, just outside Mansfield on the main road to Derby. I asked some of the "walking wounded" if they would take me out for a walk, as I was in a wheelchair. At first the sister said no, but constant requests were made and at last we were allowed out. So three lads on crutches one morning set out to push me around the woodlands – what a wonderful event. All went well until we came to the hill that went down to the main road, where I began to pick up a bit of speed. The brake on my wheelchair acted only on one wheel, and I knew that I was going too fast to apply it. I would have spun round and most certainly come to grief. So I let it go. Then it was too late to stop at all. Down the hill I went at great speed, straight across the main road into the ditch the other side, head first, wheelchair now on top of me. I had got over a main road without being hit by anything. Unbelievable. I looked up to see three blokes running (?) down the hill on crutches. I just started to laugh at this sight that will not often have been seen. Back in the ward, a furious sister was to be avoided whenever possible for the next few days. I was pretty "shook up", but still smile at those three guys desperately trying to catch up.

Whilst I was in Harlow Wood Hospital, the sister came and asked if I would go and talk to a new patient who was being very uncooperative (why me?). Well, I wandered down the ward to see "Wilf" and sat by him and asked how he was – no response. Could I do anything for him – no response. Would he like a game of draughts – no response. Ok. I get up to go, turn away and he says "Can you play chess?" "Sorry, no." "Right," he says, "I will teach you!" I went to get the chess set, and over the next few weeks I learnt to play, or at least learnt the moves! Wilf would play without his queen but was still light years in front of me. During this time, I was to learn that

Wilf had served life for murder! He had come home on leave unexpectedly and found his wife in bed with someone else. He told me about life in jail, and how he coped with the solitude. He said that he went on journeys. He would decide where to go and then lie on his bed and, leaving his body there, he would drift out and go on his travels! His worst fear was not knowing how long his prison term would be; he could not count the days and years down as life could be anything up to twenty-one years. I like to think that our talks helped Wilf to cope with life. I never saw him again after I left hospital. The sister told me later, at one of my outpatient appointments, that she had known Wilf had been in prison but was not allowed to tell me at the time.

Myfanwy was now running the farm; what a bad time it must have been, with my regular visits to hospital and hobbling on one foot and one hand not useable. I can tell you it was very frustrating, but with the help of friends, we slowly got back into harness again, but were desperately short of money.

Men had been paid to do work that I should have been doing with no extra money coming in. My insurance company had only helped when I was away in hospital, I got nothing while I was at home. Because I was not totally incapacitated, they said I could still run the farm and give orders so I was not entitled. Lesson No. 3: never ever trust an insurance company.

One of my best friends at this time was my neighbour Bob Pope and his wife Peggy. Bob was the first person that I met when I came to Springs Farm. He farmed the farm at one end of our drive, and he had called in just as we were unloading the furniture into the house. His friendly voice boomed, "Anyone at home? I'm Bob Pope. If you need any help just give me a call." Well, we needed some help now, even though it was a while since it had been offered, and he and Peggy were a pillar of strength to us. If he reads this, he will now be wondering what's coming. It must be one of the very few times I'm at an advantage, so I must make the most of it! Well, we used to go to lots of things together and once we were going to Askham Bryan Agricultural College to listen to a lecturer. On winter nights we had got to playing table tennis – I never won a game – we had some good close games but I never won, not once. He had come for a game the day before our outing to Askham Bryan and he said, "The one who loses tonight buys dinner tomorrow." You've guessed it, I won. It was the one and only time that I was to do so, but it was the right time! On that outing to Askham Bryan we were in York and Bob said, "Look at that", and in a shop was a bag for holding clothes pegs with "Peggy Bag" embroidered on it. He said I must buy it for Peggy. Peggy was not amused and he was reminded many times – Bob's comment: "They take some pleasing, these ladies!"

On my return to work I wrote to all the people that I owed money to, to tell them my situation. I could see my way through, but if all my creditors wanted paying at once now I was back, I would be unable to do so without selling up. I wrote to the bank, feed, fertiliser and seed firms. I did not write to my landlord as he knew my situation and my rent had to be paid or I could lose my farm. It was an anxious time waiting for the replies, with many schemes going on in my head to match likely situations. I only had one firm that wanted paying before they would trade again and that was my feed company. As they were the only one, I could easily pay them up, and I was very surprised when their representative called round for his usual order. I have never liked being rude to anyone but I made an exception in this case. He was sent off with a flea in his ear.

It was at this time that I had a shock – my accountant told me that he could not act for me any more because I was insolvent and it was illegal to trade and it was his duty to tell me! So I went off to find another accountant. I had always been two years behind with my accounts; this was because stock had to be valued for tax when they were still not ready for market, so if my growing lambs were valued too high I would have to pay tax that would not have had to be paid if we had waited until sale day. Similarly, if I valued them too low I would have a lot of tax to pay when they were sold – so I liked to do my accounts when the lambs had been sold so there would be no adjustment. This situation saved me, as my new accountant said that, yes, I had been insolvent two years before but now, at this time, I was solvent again! So by pure luck I had survived this difficult time.

We had been connected with electricity at about the same time as we got water, so by now we had had it some time. Whilst the electric company were bringing the line to the farm they had felled about eight oak trees along the hedgerow. I thought this was a great pity and had tried to get them to come in another way, but it was a few hundred yards farther and they said the cost was too much. So we had these oak tree "boles" waiting for the landlord to collect. The bark was now coming off them and they had split in drying out, but it was lovely timber, so it was no surprise when a timber man appeared at the door to say that they were coming to collect them. He also said they were to fell the oak at the end of the garden to go with them. I said I did not think this was a good idea as it was such

a lovely tree, with no "stags head" in its top (i.e. dead branches stuck up out the top like a stag's horn). But he said Mr. Toulson had told him to fell it and he had come to do it. We had a discussion and, white faced, he went off to see Mr. Toulson.

The following morning I see a Rolls Royce coming down the drive! Out gets Mr. Toulson. "Morning, Trevor. How's your liver today?" "It's ok, Mr. Toulson, but it was not well yesterday." "No, so I hear! Will Myfanwy have a cup of coffee on?" "Maybe, if the news is good." I am getting too big for my boots; I can see that I am about to be taken down a peg or two. Mr. Toulson ignores this and strides towards the house. "Excuse me, Mr. Toulson, but before we go in, just take a look at this lovely oak tree…" Only a slight pause before he continues his way to the kitchen. He sits down, looks at Myfanwy and says, "Nice to see you, Mrs. Robinson. When's the happy event?"(!)

We were dumbstruck. Myfanwy had only just missed a period and we were thinking maybe we were expecting our second child, but no one knew that we were even thinking this. Over coffee, Mr. Toulson said that he was pleased we had settled in and that he liked to see a young family in his farm – it gave stability, and encouraged the farmer to extra effort so that he would not have time to question things that were not his concern. But in this case, he was right and he could keep his tree! Mr. Toulson left, with the remark, "I hope it's another boy – I have another farm." I thanked him and said, "Myfanwy wants a girl." And with "Let me know how things go", he was gone.

SHEEP HAVE ALWAYS been my "first love" and they have played a big part in my life. The first sheep that I brought with me from Herefordshire were little Welsh ewes and they were just the wrong breed for me now. So they went and my new breed were mules, as my old Yorkshire breed at Kettlewell were also out of place on this poor lowland farm. This question of breeds is interesting. Let's have a look at it.

It's a job to know just how the sheep on our island came into being because they were here before recorded history. We do know that early man knew how to spin wool which had been shed by the sheep and weave it into a coarse fabric, because it has been found on early man. It is believed that the sheep was domesticated in about 10,000 BC, but it's difficult to say just when. Maybe in years to come it will be possible to date it with more accuracy. We do know that by the time the Romans arrived in Britain better quality wool was being used for clothes. This was improved again with the sheep brought in by the Romans. At that time, most of the wool in Britain was from sheep of the Soay type, therefore it was black or dark brown but not too coarse. This would be the start of the white-woolled sheep, as the Roman sheep were much lighter in colour than our native sheep. About this time, during the first century AD, the early steps would have been taken in selective improvement, and over the next thousand years, the distinctive types of sheep would have evolved around Britain, giving us the wonderful spread of breeds that we see today.

It is often said that several of our high mountain sheep breeds came from sheep swimming ashore from Spanish ships

wrecked off our coastline, but it is more likely that they were brought by invading Norsemen and the like. Great strides were made by the abbeys: Fountains Abbey in Yorkshire was reputed to have had more than 30,000 sheep in its care during the tenth and eleventh centuries. They were kept by the monks on granges, so if you see a farm today called "something Grange" in Yorkshire, it was probably a sheep farm owned by Fountains Abbey at one time. The monks must have appreciated what a wonderful animal the sheep is. Look at a few of the things it gave them: wool for spinning and making into clothes (for many years wool had been exported to Rome for the fine robes of emperors); the skin of the sheep for clothes, thongs and shoes (even today, lamb skin is used for making fine gloves); milk fresh for drinking, to make into butter and cheese; the horns for making into drinking cups and hunting horns; bone to make into instruments like needles and combs; fat to make into tallow candles and, of course, meat. All meat eaten at this time was mutton, unlike today when most sheep meat is lamb.

I'm sure I have missed a few things out, but the list shows what a useful animal the sheep was. The breeds by now had been segregated into various types, mainly mountain, moor and lowland, and there are fifty-four different breeds native to Britain today. There are also eight well-known accepted half-breeds and eight recently imported breeds from the Continent (most of these, in my opinion, not needed). To complete the list of sheep in Britain today there are three Southern Hemisphere breeds. A grand total of seventy-three different types.

Looking at these in more detail, we will start with the mountain breeds. These are the sheep that are born and bred on the mountain. They are a tough lot, used to plenty of rain, cold and snow, existing on low-quality heather and coarse grass. In my opinion, they live in the most beautiful parts of Britain, but I don't expect that they often admire the view! At lambing time it takes one hundred ewes to produce eighty lambs, half of which are, of course, male, so they are not prolific breeders. Of the main breeds, there are Blackface, found mostly in Scotland, Cheviot from Northumberland and Scotland, North Country Cheviot from Sutherland and Caithness, Brecknock Cheviot from the Brecon Beacons, Exmoor Horn from southwest England, Herdwick from the Lake District, Lonk from the Pennines, Derbyshire Gritstone from the Peak District, Welsh Hill Speckled Face, Welsh Mountain, Black Welsh Mountain, South Welsh Mountain, all found in Wales, with the minor breed of Welsh Mountain Badger Faced. These are the real mountain breeds with coarse wool containing a lot of kemp. Kemp is not wool but a coarse hair which helps to run the rain water off the fleece. It will not dye as this also runs off. It is quite noticeable in Harris Tweed.

The next category is the moorland or hill type. The main breeds are: Beulah Speckled Face, Kerry Hill, Radnor Hill, all found on the Welsh borderlands; Dalesbred, Rough Fell, Swaledale are found in the Yorkshire Dales, with the minor breeds Wensleydale and Teeswater; the Dartmoor and the White Faced Dartmoor from Dartmoor, Blue Faced Leicester from around Hexham. These sheep, like the mountain breeds, live on the heather and coarse grass of the moor and the low-quality grass of the hill. Their lambing percentage is also about 80%. They are born and bred on the moor; this means that they are "hefted" and have to stay on the land even if the farmer moves. They also live in wonderful country (I know because I used to be a shepherd in the Yorkshire Dales). The wool from these breeds is also of a coarse variety, much of it being sold to China and Russia for mattresses.

Our next category is the lowland sheep. These breeds are the ones able to make the most of the much better grazing in fields and valley bottoms. They include all the 'Down' breeds: Dorset, Hampshire, South Down, Suffolk, Romney, Ryeland, Shropshire, Llanwern, and the Oxford, coupled with the Clun Forest, Devon Closewool and, believe it or not, the Shetland.

These are the main, tight solid-wool breeds with no kemp to spoil the sample, really good quality wool. There is another part of the lowland section with not such a good fleece but with other qualities such as being good mothers and meat producers. These include Border Leicester, Dorset Horn and Lleyn. Also in this group is the Blue Faced Leicester. That is strange because we have already got it in the moorland section. This is because it was developed in the hills around Hexham but now it is common all over the country as a wonderful crossing ram with any of the mountain breeds, producing excellent mothers for the production of fat lambs (which in my opinion are the best in all the world).

There is yet another category. These are the Longwools, the Devon and Cornwall Longwools, Leicester, Lincoln and the Cotswold Longwools. These sheep have long twisty and beautifully lustred wool. Some sheep from the moor group also have this type of wool, such as the Teeswater, Wensleydale and, yes, once again, the Blue Faced Leicester!

This leaves just three of the main and minor breeds. These are the Jacob, which is found all over the country, often in small flocks, kept for the multicoloured fleece that is mostly used by home spinners for distinctive individual garments. The British milk sheep produces milk for fresh consumption or to be made into Roquefort-type cheese. It also has a medium quality wool. The last is the poor old Wiltshire Horn, which has no wool at all! It sheds its bit of wool in early spring and most of it ends up on the barbed wire around the field. Well, maybe the local birds will be pleased to find it for their nests. The Wiltshire Horn does produce some very good fat lambs for the market.

We have so far looked at the main and minor breeds of Britain. There is also a small group of rare breeds. These were once thriving breeds in their own environment but have got left behind owing to better types becoming more widespread. We do not want to lose these unique breeds as they may be very important in future breeding programmes with their own genetic make-up. Most of these rare breeds come from Scotland – even the Manx Loaghtan – the others are the Boreray–Hebridean (on St. Kilda) – North Ronaldsay (on Orkney) and the Soay. These are all tough little sheep that used to live in inhospitable places and on sea shores around Scotland. All are dark brown or black and would be difficult to find in their natural terrain. The English rare breeds are the Norfolk Horn and the Portland from the lowlands and the White Faced Woodland from the Derbyshire moors. This is only a short list of eight sheep breeds but very important all the same. We are indebted to the people who keep these breeds going.

An even smaller group is the three Southern Hemisphere sheep. These include the Merino, which was developed in Spain in the first century by a Roman called Columella. The breed is now the main type in Australia and parts of New Zealand. The other two breeds are the Polwarth, developed in Australia from the Merino, and the Corriedale, bred in New Zealand from the Merino. British farmers did try to establish the Merino in this country but it really did better in the dryer or arid countries. There are now just a few small flocks kept here.

I am afraid that I am one of those people who believe British stock is unbeatable. We have the weather for it; we have the technical back-up and the farmers to carry out the expert requirements for unbeatable stock breeding. Look around the world; in Argentina the huge herds of beef cattle are Herefords. In New Zealand, Australia and the United States of America, the cattle are all "the white-faced uns", the Hereford. Thousands and thousands of cattle all originated in Britain. Getting back to the sheep, the picture is even more pronounced. The Shropshire is found in the USA, Canada, Australia and New Zealand; the Ryeland in Australia, New Zealand and South America; the Lincoln Longwool in Argentina; the Leicester Longwool in Australia and New Zealand; the South Down is the basis of all the New Zealand sheep.

Australia – and, wait for it – FRANCE; the Hampshire Down is a fine sheep producing fine wool in Australia, New Zealand, the USA and South Africa; the Dorset Horn, like the Hampshire Down but including Canada; the Dorset Down in Australia, New Zealand and Argentina; the Cheviot (used to be called the Linton) in Canada, Scandinavia, the USA, South Africa and New Zealand. Last but not least, the Border Leicester is found in Australia, New Zealand, South Africa and North and South America. With stock like this, why on earth do we import breeds from the Continent? If we were using them to improve our stock, yes. But they are not doing that; they are watering our good stock down into a mish-mash of indefinable breeds. We are losing the identity of our flocks and this does not bode well for the future.

Now I have got that off my chest, I will continue with my list of breeds in the UK with a category of recent introductions. They are the Bleu de Maine, Charollais, Vendeen, Ile de France and Rouge de L'ouest, all from France, with the Texel from France and Holland, the Oldenburg from West Germany, the Friesland from the Friesland Isles. I have no doubt that these are fine sheep in their own environment but I do wish they were not here. Aren't I a miserable, narrow-minded old sod?!

To finish on a much more happy note, let's look at the accepted crosses that have acquired their own names. The Colbred is a hybrid sheep from Gloucestershire that has now become a breed but is only found in small numbers.

Dalesbred Ram by P. Lynes

The Cambridge is a unique sheep developed at Cambridge University – farmers throughout Britain sent ewes that had continuously lambed triplets to Cambridge. These were all pooled together and the Cambridge was born. It is a breed that has "litters" rather than singles or doubles (you can probably sense that I am not a lover of these two breeds). The next three are the English, Scottish and Welsh half-breeds. These are fine, well-proportioned sheep; good mothers with plenty of milk for the lambs. The English half-breed is the lamb of a Clun Forest ewe and Border Leicester ram. The Scottish half-breed has the Cheviot ewe as a mother and the Border Leicester as a dad. The Welsh half-breed has the same Border Leicester ram crossed with a Welsh Mountain ewe. The wool from all these three crosses was used for hosiery, knitwear and tweeds.

Good as they are, these breeds have, I believe, been superseded by the mules. I find that the Mule has a better percentage of lambs which more than makes up for the slightly better wool quality of the half-breeds. All the mules have the same breed of ram, the Blue Faced Leicester. The English or North Country Mule has either the Swaledale or possibly the Dalesbred ewe as a mother. I cannot be too high in my praise of these sheep. They are just super in all ways. The Scottish Mule has a Blackface ewe mother and the Welsh Mule has any of the Welsh Mountain ewes as its dam. The Blue Faced Leicester is not a good-looking sheep but the result of his crossing capacity is out of all proportion to his looks. I don't know how it works, but it is a fine cross. Another of the good cross-bred ewes that also comes from Yorkshire (I wonder why I like these Yorkshire sheep?) is the Masham. This is bred by crossing a Teeswater or Wensleydale ram with a Swaledale or Dalesbred ewe. The result is a black-and-white face and a fleece like ringlets that just about touches the ground. It is a very good mother to its lambs, does very well on grass fields but is no good for feeding on roots.

I think it's a wonderful situation that we have here in Britain, all these breeds in their own little area, all with something to add to the scenic beauty of our island, looked after by farmers and shepherds who really do have the environment at heart. Long may it last.

I seem to have got carried away there. I hope you are still with me – just wait until I get started on sheep dogs!

I have extolled the joys of lambing in a previous book, but this breed of Scottish Mule (in my case, a Scots Blackface ewe and Blue Faced Leicester) are excellent mothers, and as we now lamb in yards that hold 400 ewes we have problems. The first batch that came in were the ones that lambed close together. By that I mean one after the other quickly, or many at the same time. As they were also in close proximity it was sometimes hard to tell which lambs belonged to which ewe. As these ewes were such good mothers they would often take to lambs which belonged to another ewe. So you would often get two ewes taking to the same lamb and taking no interest in any lambs they had given birth to earlier. Ewes would take off with another ewe's lambs and leave her own for the other ewe and she would not have them. So with several ewes lambing all at the same time you had to be on your toes to pack mum and lamb off into a "mothering pen" as soon as possible or it would quickly get out of control. The "mothering pen" was made out of straw bales, two long and two wide. Mum and lamb would be popped over into these pens and the ewes could lick their lambs dry. Once this was done they were a family and there would be no more trouble in getting mixed up, so they only stayed here for 12 hours or until all the pens were full and needed for the next ewes. When they left these pens they were all put into a big six-bay Dutch barn with a three-bay lean-to so it was huge, where they all ran together. The young lambs had a great time in here running and jumping about; at two days old they were impossible to catch. At this time of year we were very busy, day and night, but we always had time for any local schools to come along to see all the action. We had to carry on working but the children loved to come, especially to feed the orphaned lambs with a bottle. Sometimes the youngsters had more milk over themselves than they got down the lambs. What their mums had to say when they got back home, I dread to think. A few days later, our postman would arrive with stacks of letters from these youngsters. They were much appreciated.

The schoolboys also liked to play with the lambs in the Dutch barn. I would say pick a lamb out and if you catch it you can have it. A bit rash, but I never lost one!

The ewes and lambs would stay in the Dutch barn as long as possible. That is, until there was no room for any more, at which point they were turned out. We needed as many people as possible to do this as it was bedlam. Ewes would dash off in any direction, trying to take her lambs off to a secluded place. The lambs had an entirely different aim, and that was to dash around as a pack and jump and charge one another and have a great time. This would set off mum charging around looking for her brood. The whole thing looked like the flock were caught up in a whirlwind. Dogs were no help at this point as the lambs had not yet been made aware of the dogs' role. They would run and jump over the dogs, or run with them or even chase them. So it was quite a long job getting them all into the one field where we wanted them. We even used to wait until the postman came so we had an extra hand! You can tell that by the time the third batch left the lambing yards some nine weeks later, we were happy but pretty tired. Nevertheless, what a wonderful time.

In my years at Springs Farm I made many farming friends. One of these was a very good stock farmer called Jack Badger. I called on him one day and he said, "Come and look at these beef cattle and tell me what you think." We went down to his yards and there was a bunch of superb young fit cattle. They were beautiful, they just shone. They were coal black with a bit of white on them. I said, "Something to be proud of there, Jack." "Yes," he said, "but you are a stockman, tell me what breed they are."

I was on the spot. "Well, they are a cross…" "Yes, which?" "Well… er… mother's Friesian, not Holstein, they are too compact for Holstein, right?… Bull, must be a real good one – what about Devon?" (I knew that he liked Devon beef cattle.) "Well done," said Jack. "You've played a blinder there!"

Back in the farmhouse, we had a cup of tea and, as I got up to go home, Jack said, "Them cattle, they are Belted Galloway cross Angus. Cheers!"

I was to remember this some time later as I stood at Jack's graveside at his burial. It was a very cold winter's day, and we'd had the service in church and now it was the interment. Jack had been a big man, 6'5" tall, and it was really no surprise when the grave digger had not made the grave big enough and Jack got stuck! There were many people there and it was embarrassing. Jack's son, also called Jack, was standing next to the vicar, and he looked at him and said, "He always was an awkward b— when he was alive." Typical of this old breed of stockmen.

Jack was buried in December and David, my new son, was born in December; if he was a replacement for Jack, I hoped he would be as good a stockman. Myfanwy had once again had a bad time and went into Doncaster for a few days to recover. She really did want a girl but it was not to be. But it was soon forgotten as David was a smashing lad, who was always smiling. (No, it was not wind.) So Mr. Toulson had been right – how did these old boys know? They were real characters. Where are they now? I suppose most of them were practical men who gained a huge amount of knowledge through working experience, so would know from "hands-on" working.

My friend Bob Pope was always coming out with witty sayings and little snippets of wisdom, and I used to think "that's clever"; my mind was unable to match his wit. That is, until one Christmas when Bob made the mistake of giving me a year's subscription to *Readers Digest*. He said that it might increase my education (nice of him!). But, unfortunately for Bob, I noticed on the bottom of each page there was a little gem of a quotation!

One of my rugby-playing friends in Herefordshire was John James. He in turn had a friend called Derek Lloyd (later to captain England twice) who ran dogs in sheep dog trials. John was also engaged in running at sheep dog trials. They went to most trials together and one time when the English National was run near Worksop they came to stay with us at the farm. So I went along to watch them run; since my disastrous one and only run at Amestry many years before, I had not been to a trial. Well, these two were (and still are) very enthusiastic and as they were at the farm for two nights, sheep dogs were at the top of things discussed. They took me to the international meeting at the Old Bell at Barnby Moor after the last run at Welbeck, where there was a lively meeting. Their parting words when they left were "get a dog and have a go". What did they mean "get a dog", I had five! My dogs were working dogs and they were good. I had one bitch called Glen (?) – she could put 400 sheep into a pen that should only hold 200. This was better than any trial dog could do, but in my case it was hard graft, while with the trial dog it's grace and style that matter. So it's a different ball game.

Whilst at the Welbeck trial, I had met local people who were interested in sheep dog trials, especially one called Eric Whitehead. I suppose I was drawn to him because he is a real character – a lovely man, just full of enthusiasm for sheep dogs. It did not take Eric long to realise that he had a chance to get a few of us together, and so the Retford and District Sheep Dog Society was born. It's many years now since training days were held at Springs Farm. We had members that had no sheep but just a border collie, who desperately wanted to have a try at trialling. They were at a big disadvantage because to do well, a dog must work sheep every day. It's a credit to them that most found someone with sheep near them who – once the dog was under control – would let them practise. They came to me because I had sheep that I had bought specially to train dogs on, rough sheep that cost a few shillings at market because they were cast-offs. After worming and being put on to good pasture some of these grew into good sheep and often made more profit than those that cost a lot more. But they were only used for a short time and then sold on.

We held these training days about one day a month; Eric was the trainer as he was the only one with a fully trained dog. It was called Drift, an all-white dog, and it was to help train many dogs. I remember one such training day, early on, when an enthusiastic new member arrived with his dog. Eric would tackle any situation – his only condition being that the dog should stop when told to do so.

The first question: "Will he stop when told?" Handler: "Yes, he's very good." Eric: "Ok, let's see what he can do." The handler goes to post with Eric standing behind him. "Ok, set him off."

Handler: "Away, Ben." Dog runs straight at six sheep that have been let out of a trailer about 25 yards away. Eric: "Stop your dog." Handler: "Lie down, Ben." No response. Eric: "Stop your b— dog!" Handler: "Lie down, LIE DOWN, LIE DOWN...OH dear..."

By this time, the sheep have decided that they are not playing this game – two have jumped the hedge into a neighbour's corn field – two have raced off down the drive – one is hiding under the trailer and one is being firmly held by its throat by the dog.

Drift had earned his dinner by the time eight hopefuls had had their turn at "the post", and then showing how it should be done and returning the sheep back to the safety of their field. It was quite amazing how these enthusiasts kept on going with one disaster after another, but they did, and over the weeks, good improvement was made. Many sandwiches and gallons of tea later, the short training field was changed for a longer field, one able to be used for a small sheep dog trial. Most of the society were able to get round the course and get penned. Indeed, three members went on to win the Bolton Cup at Bamford, run by the famous Longshaw Sheep Dog Society. Better still, one of our lady members went on to get into the English National Team and represented England at the International. That means that she was one of the top fifteen in the country that year. There are about 150 competitors all trying to get into the team. And they have to qualify to get into the 150.

Those early days with Eric were not only hard work but good fun. Plenty of "ragging" one another, and we all had high hopes that our dogs would be world beaters.

I seem to have got a bit ahead of myself here, as I had one of the most torrid times of my life in 1958. Myfanwy was busy bringing up two strapping boys, one of whom, John, was now at school. He was at Misson school, a small village in Nottinghamshire – there were 250 people living in the whole parish, about 1,000-plus acres. There were seventeen farmers in the village. It was a hive of activity. Small and big farmers, most milking various sizes of herds. John used to get the school bus in the morning and we had had a bit of a job to get him on it. Our farm was over half a mile from the road – but we had two ways to it. If he walked down one drive he was too near to Misson to be allowed on the bus – if he walked down the other drive he was allowed on the bus, because it was further away from the school. The education committee said he must walk down the first drive – thereby meaning that he would have to walk the 1½ miles to school and the bus would pass him by. The bus was never even half full! It took a journey to Nottingham to get some sense into the situation. It was stated that the distance travelled down the drive was not counted! Finally, it was measured on the county map and the farmhouse was a few hundred yards over the two miles minimum, so he was allowed to travel by bus just so long as it was not full. Lesson No. 4: never try to understand government committees.

But I digress, mostly because I don't know how to explain my feelings. Well, Myfanwy had managed to get pregnant again (I don't know how – it just happened). The problem was she had been quite ill the first time and very ill the second time.

We were told that she should not have any more children, as they expected it to be life-threatening. Now, Myfanwy was not a sickly person; she was fit and well and a picture of health and it did not seem possible for there to be anything to worry about, but I do not know about these things. If I am unwell I just ask the vet next time he comes! The doctor advises her to have an abortion. We ask for a second opinion and get one. Still the same answer. My reaction is OK, we have got two fine boys, we are very lucky, let's not tempt bad luck. Myfanwy is part of my life, we have been through some tough times together and have won through, so we will get through this one as well. My mind is made up for abortion. Myfanwy's mind is made up – she is going to have this baby because it's going to be a girl and this is her last chance. How on earth does she work out that it's going to be a girl? – Because she has had two boys and this seems different! (Nearly said Lesson No. 5: never try to understand female logic.) "Myfanwy, the chances are 50/50." – "Yes, I know, but this is a girl." We (?) decide to risk it and I am not happy. Our doctor is not happy. We all think it's too big a risk. Myfanwy will not now discuss it, as it's been decided. As time goes on, we plan and work – a bed is booked in a nursing home – Mum and Dad arrange a midwife to come and live in with us for a few weeks before, and an auntie will come for a few weeks after the expected birth. I really do have a bad feeling about this – too much care is being taken. It's a daft thing to say – but that's how it feels.

The day arrives at last. Ms Bottomley, the midwife, takes over and sends for the doctor. Orders are barked at me, fetch this and get that ready, we are off to the nursing home, the doctor will be there and waiting. I am tempted to salute as I dash off to get the car. Midwife, doctor and Myfanwy are safely at the nursing home. Nurse Bottomley tells me to go and get some work done! It will be an hour or two yet before Myfanwy has her daughter. I understand that doctor, midwife and the nursing home staff do a wonderful job, but when I am at last allowed to see Myfanwy, I get a shock. This healthy fit person that only a few hours ago (12 to be exact) was rosy-cheeked is now white and weak and obviously not very well at all. Myfanwy was in the nursing home for five weeks, but I am pleased to say when she came home she improved fast and was very happy to have Helen Jane all to herself. We were now one complete and happy family.

We are lucky in the British Isles to have so much fascinating history. It does not take a journey of much distance to find some interesting happening. In Kettlewell it was mining of lead that left its mark; the lead was sent to Rome to adorn many roofs. Herefordshire, a most rural of counties, has the Mappa Mundi, one of the first maps of the world (with Hereford as its centre!?). Also the wonderful Hereford cattle, as we've already seen, are now worldwide. So now, what would I be able to find in a flat barren area on the Yorkshire–Nottingham borders? Well, just five miles from the farm is Epworth, a small agricultural village where John Wesley was born and brought up. Myfanwy, being Welsh, was a staunch Methodist, as were her Mum and Dad. We only had a small chapel in Misson with just eight members but it was a mini whirlwind; many events took place there. My daughter will kill me for this, but she was once May Queen;

we have got some historic pictures of this event even though Helen has been hell-bent on destroying them for years. Her mum was very proud. Myfanwy was the secretary/treasurer, aisle person (collected the offerings), harmonium player and cleaner of the chapel, and did this work for many years. Her commitment to the chapel was total and she got great support from her religion. I was never able to accept the religious side but I used to support all the events with much enthusiasm, and I believe this was appreciated. So it must have been nice for Myfanwy to be living so close to the founder of her religion.

Another bit of history of the area, just on the border in Nottinghamshire, was Scrooby (what a great name). This was where William Brewster farmed. He was the leader – or one of the leaders – of the pilgrim fathers, who were being persecuted because of their religion, and decided to take off to America. He went with one of his neighbours, John (or was it William?) Bradford, whose farm was even closer to mine (about two miles away). They had a rough time in England and a rougher time when they arrived in America. These events hold a fascination for me; the times when they took place were hard and they must have been exceptional characters and strong men to have endured them.

Bawtry, our nearest shopping centre, has got a very interesting history; although it is 30 to 40 miles from the sea, it used to be a port! The boats coming from Sweden, Norway and Denmark would sail up the Humber then up the Trent and so up the river Idle to Bawtry. They mostly brought iron ore, which was then taken by pack horse to Sheffield. Taken out from Bawtry would be grain and timber from Sherwood Forest. This was a very busy time – not like the Bawtry of today. You may have heard that many of the old houses that were built of oak were built using old ship's timbers. Well, maybe a few were, but in the days of the felling of timber from Sherwood Forest, the timber was graded by quality and one of the grades was "ship's timber", in other words, good enough to be used for making ships (which were made of oak in those days). This grade would also be used for building houses, so although this timber was "ship's timber" grade it would not have already been used for this purpose.

An acquaintance of mine bought a big old house in Wharf Street in Bawtry. It had not been renovated for many years, so he set about improving it. In one large room facing the street, he found a large board covering the whole of one wall. When cleaned, it revealed the times of departure and arrivals for ships with details of their cargos from the eighteenth century! Bawtry at this time was also on the Great North Road, with the Crown being a posting house. Going south to Barnby Moor is the Old Bell, another post house (a favourite hotel where Winston Churchill loved to go). If you go south from here again where parts of the Great North Road can still be seen, it is so narrow that a car would now have a job to go down it, even if it were cleared of the old hedges that now just about meet in the middle of the road. A little further along – just west of Retford – is Jockey House, outside of which there is a huge signpost about seven feet tall and four feet square, built of stone, pointing to Yorke, London and Worksoppe. Just past here, the old road was lost when an aerodrome was built during the war. Bawtry must have been a very busy and important place in those days. The road went north from Bawtry to Hatfield, not far from my farm, and I was bemused when I learned that this stretch of the North Road had the trees on each side of it cut down for fifty yards to stop the highwaymen from holding up the stage coaches, as much trouble had been caused, with the robbers escaping to Misson through the marshes! Well – enough of that!

The land to the north-east of the farm going towards Epworth used to be a swamp. Indeed, the high ground there is still called the Isle of Axeholm, and it was once an island. The people in this area made their living by fishing, wild fowling and guiding travellers through the wetlands. That was until the King sold off this land to a Dutchman called Vermuyden, who started to drain it for farmland. This would mean that most of the locals would lose their living, so war broke out between them and the Irish labourers digging the big drains. The Dutchman persevered and, over many years, the land was drained and is now fertile farmland growing potatoes, red beet, carrots, sugar beet and wheat. The Isle of Axeholm in the middle of this old swamp is now one of the few places in Britain that is still farmed in the old "strip" system and is well worth a visit.

Life was getting into a routine at the farm with milking, sheep, and arable. We had been milking for a good many years now, but with never more than thirty cows and usually about twenty. So we were not a big producer but we were still milking for the monthly milk cheque, which was a life saver, but it also brought its problems. We milked direct into milk churns which had to be cooled as soon as possible. This was done by placing a hollow U-shaped tube into the churn, which had a lid that over-covered the top of the churn; this part that overlapped had holes all round the underside, in the middle of the lid, and on top was an inlet for water. (Are you still with me?) The water entered through this by a pipe connected to a tap. The water turned the hollow tube in the milk, which then was returned and flowed down the outside of the churn, via the holes around the top. This was ok in winter (when it was less urgent) because the water was cold, but in summer the water was not so cold, so it took a long time to cool the milk. We usually had about six or seven churns and often the milk lorry would arrive before the milk was all cold (I had managed to be first pick-up again). We did get some churns back the next morning. Because of this, we had to buy a "freezer bank", which got rid of the problem but it was still unsatisfactory. The time came when milk was piped direct into a bulk tank which was refrigerated and the dairies would no longer pick up churns but instead came round with a tanker and the milk was pumped into this. This hit me in several ways – the first, of course, was the cost of buying the bulk system. Next, the tanker would not come down my gated lane. Then there was the size of my herd, it was just not big enough, and again the capital cost to make it larger was too great. So we decided to go out of milk (or was it decided for us?) and go all sheep with arable as well. It was a big step for us as we would lose the monthly milk cheque. Whatever should we do – could we still carry on? The day came – the cows went – and, to our surprise, so did most of our crippling bills. Instead of being under the great strain sharing out the milk cheque and trying to save a bit for ourselves, we were able to relax and enjoy life at a slower pace. We had gone extensive instead of intensive and we never missed that milk cheque.

BOB POPE AND I were keen to start a cricket team in the village and set about getting a ground and the villagers to help establish one. Bob was a good bat (that's a fiver you owe me, Bob) and I bowled, so we had a start. It's surprising that once a start is made, many people want to help. There had been a cricket team in Misson before the war but no one had started it again afterwards, but once the inaugural meeting had taken place we were off to a flier. In this small village there were some really good cricketers. There were five from the same family, the Smiths, who were the core of our first games. We had to start by getting a field. This was the big problem. Fortunately for us, the foreman of a local farming company based in Misson was a keen and very good cricketer and he was able to secure a field for us. We were away.

Next was money (the bane of my life). Well, we got this idea of an Ox Roast; Springs Farm was to be the venue, as we had two large yards, one covered and one half-covered. Through a large stone barn (we always called it the stone barn even though it was brick), there was a six-bay Dutch barn, that is 90 feet by 30 feet, which would be ideal for a dance. We knew nothing about ox roasting so we thought we would ask Scunthorpe Technical College Catering students if they would like to use the occasion for experience. I spoke to the head of the department on the phone and he said it would be fantastic for his students. A few days later, there was a knock at the kitchen door and there stood a man in a suit with a briefcase in his hand. I thought, "Blimey, a tax inspector" – but no, it was the head of the department coming to talk about the cooking of the ox. He came in, opened his briefcase and produced sheets of papers on the project. It was unbelievable – the bullock (ox) had to be killed in a certain way so that all four legs were in the standing position, not hung up by the hind legs as normal. When set in this position, the spit would be able to turn the beast in the best way for roasting. The spit would have to be a three-inch diameter scaffolding pole with a cartwheel attached at one end to turn the ox. The two supports at each end of the spit would have to be 4'6" off the ground. Two lots of 56-pound weights attached to the cartwheel by chains and hooks were needed to control the turning of the spit. The fire would have to be 5 feet long and 2 feet wide with a curved back plate to reflect the heat – we would need so many cwt of coal then so many cwt of smokeless fuel. The fire would have to be lit at 6 a.m., and it would take x hours to roast the 6 cwt beast. It would feed 500 people at so much each – we would need so much various salads – so many bread rolls

– so much salad dressing – so many plates, knives and forks. It was endless, the pile of papers grew until they covered the table, and still it went on – so many students – the meat cut in this way and that – so much salt, pepper – it would be a good idea to cut off so many pounds of silverside and cook it in the ovens at the Tech – just in case the time factor was a bit slow – his students would be there at 8 a.m. when the fire would be at such and such a temperature – too low a heat it would take too long to cook and go "rancid"… On and on he went, until at last he said, "I think that's about it." "Good," I said. "I'm glad I asked you. We would never have put that package together. I suppose when you do it regularly, it's easier." "Never done one before," he said, "but it will be fine."

Once again, I was head first into a situation way beyond me, but we had a lot of help, and things slowly took shape. A four-wheeled trailer was found for the band to play on – straw bales arranged all round the Dutch barn, and rows of bales in the stone barn – the fireplace was made – the spit was made, trestle tables put up – the students kept bringing piles of stuff and cutting salads up. The bullock had been killed two weeks before and hung in its unusual position. The meat had been cut off and taken to be cooked at Scunthorpe. This was cleverly done as it was cut from the inside of the legs and it was not possible to detect any difference except by close examination.

The great day arrived. The fire was lit at 6 a.m., just under the roof in the half-covered yard. By 7.30 a.m. the roof was very hot and started to smoke! It was all I could do to pull the fire out into the open; it's a good job that the ox had not yet been put into place in front or the roof would have gone up in flames. As it was, it was very difficult because the fire was so hot, but a couple of tractor chains and the tractor did the job. The roof was hosed down, and we were back on track but now outside so we hoped for the weather to stay dry. The bullock was put in place with a huge drip tray under it. The spit had been altered so it now had a cartwheel on each end with the weights on one side holding the spit from going clockwise and the weights on the other side stopping it going counterclockwise. It was turned by the students, every 15 minutes, by someone on each end unhooking one chain one way and the other the opposite way onto the next spoke; it was not easy to turn, but after the first hour they got the knack and all went well.

Throughout the day, bowls full of salad were made, four trestle tables full, with bowls full of bread rolls – stacks of plates, cups and saucers and cutlery with piles of serviettes. It looked a picture, with chefs' tall hats in great abundance.

Night time arrived and we were ready – much to my surprise. Cars started to come down the drive and the paddock filled up. With the cars came 500 people. It was a hectic night, the ox was perfect, three chefs at a time were carving and the taste was beautiful. Crowds of people were having a really good time. I was walking through the stone barn when this voice said, "What a wonderful night, Trevor, are we insured for such an event?" Yes, it was Mr. Toulson. I had no idea he knew about it; I did not mention the roof!

I went to bed at 12 midnight, deadbeat, and in my last round to see that all was well it was nice to see, sat around the now dead but still warm fire, a group of people picking at the carcass of the bullock. In the morning, the skeleton of the ox was pure white with not a scrap of meat on it. At 10 a.m. three minibuses arrived from Scunthorpe and they made short work of clearing up – they were fantastic. Over a pot of tea in the kitchen later, they were to enthuse over the event; they had

had a great time. They were 18 or 19 years old – well done, Scunthorpe Technical College.

So the cricket club was off to a good start. A pavilion was made and put up – the square was coached into a fair state and fixtures were made. There was an old man in Misson who had played cricket for the village before the First World War – His name Hibbard Laister – and he loved to come up to watch us when we were at home. He would come and sit down by the pavilion and tell us about games long gone by. Even in those days, there were a few of the Smith family in the team. He was at one game and he started this tale about playing against Blyth, a team about ten miles away. When he told a tale he went into this kind of trance and we could see that he was reliving the game. His opening statement was – we all got on our bikes and away we went. Then we won the toss and batted first. Smithy opened – got off to a flying start as did Bill(?). They were having a rare old time and Smithy reached 50 – send a pigeon off to Misson – Bill not long after hit a six to reach 50 – send a pigeon off to Misson. And so it went on right through the match. You were waved aside if you tried to interrupt, so when he had finished he was quite out of breath. I said, "Hibbard, what's this pigeon lark?" "Oh," he said, "we always took a box of pigeons on the back of the bike, as there were many people back at the loft waiting for news of the match."

IT HAS ALWAYS been a difficult job counting sheep, even when there are only a couple of hundred of them. The usual way is to count them whilst they are being moved from field to field, as the gate can be widened or closed to regulate the flow and make it constant. That's the idea, at any rate. In fact, when the gate is pushed to stop a surge there is usually a bunch that get through, so quick counting is needed. It would not be so hard if they stayed on the ground, but they do not; many jump up in the air and often land crossways onto the flow. If you are at, say, 168, and this bunch comes through, it's odds on that you will lose count, so you have to start again and try to do better next time. Matt Middlemiss, my old boss at Kettlewell, was a master at counting so he usually took the job on. My job would be to keep the 'flow' as smooth as possible, but I would also try to count as a check. I don't think I was ever right – by the pathetic look I usually got. Mr. Middlemiss used to count in a strange language and always had a few stones in his hand. I could only remember yan, tan, tethera, that being one, two three, and it's only recently that I was able to find out the full story. I did a radio broadcast from BBC York and from this came the answer. It seems as though there were many of these local counting systems; some almost the same.

Mr. Whitehead, from whom most of my information came, has so far identified about twenty, covering the Dales, Lake District, Derbyshire, Wales and Cornwall. His information fits in well with experience. So the full count that Mr. Middlemiss used was yan, tan, tethera, methera, pip, sethera, lethera, hovera, covera, dick, yanadick, tanadick, tetheradick, metheradick, bumfit, yanabum, tanabum, tetherabum, metherabum, jigget. That is from one to twenty. This seems to be the full extent of the system. As sheep, and many other things, were often bought by the score (20), this fits into the picture well, so 120 sheep would be 6 score, and so on. Matt Middlemiss would know to within two score how many sheep we should have. We did, of course, not know exactly how many we had as there would always be a few strays to allow for. So if we were expecting, say, 100 sheep at the count, Matt would pick up seven small stones. Every time he counted to jigget (20) he would drop a stone. So when 100 sheep had gone through the count, he would have two stones left in his hand. If there were, say, ten strays in the flock he would still have two stones in his hand but his count would be up to "dick" when the sheep were all through, so this would be added on, making 110. It is simple and so much easier to just count up to twenty, whereas I was trying to count 101, 102, 103. Thanks, Mr. Whitehead, for bringing those memories back, and thanks also to BBC Radio York.

Springs Farm is a light land farm, sand and gravel, that's why Stephen Toulsons owned it. I had a constant battle trying to grow corn on this land. We would always have a good spring. The corn would chit and grow well up to May (this was when I liked the bank manager to call) and it usually looked good. June was our most important time; if we had rain in June we would have a good crop, i.e. 25 to 30 cwt per acre (good arable farms would get two tons per acre), but if no rain fell at this time our yield would be less than a ton. As my seed cost was the same as that of a good farm and my fertiliser cost was more than the good farm owing to trying to gain more yield (if a good farm put as much fertiliser on as I did, his crop would "lodge", i.e. go down, so the advantage would be lost), my total cost would be more and my risk would be higher, because of the necessity of rain in June. So year after year, we would be on tenterhooks in June. There was an irony here, as in June we also made hay! So we wanted fine weather. You will often have heard it said that the weather is always wrong for farmers. I used to say that I always got it right as I could not be wrong for both crops. Every silver lining has a cloud. So, year after year, we either made £1,000 profit or lost £1,000. But we lived well and had a wonderful life, the youngsters had a lovely environment to grow up in. I hoped that my anxiety over money did not overshadow this situation. It's a strange thing that when we were very short of cash we lived well. I had a neighbour who grew potatoes so I could always get a bag of damaged ones. I also had a twelve-bore shotgun and (although I was not a shooting man) I was never without a box of cartridges. So in these times of money shortage I would go out and shoot a rabbit, wood pigeon, hare, partridge, pheasant or duck, so you can see we ate like kings. Then, of course, we always had a lamb to kill, but this meant losing that income, so that was the last resort. We did sometimes eat lamb!

Since getting the urge to sheep dog trial, things had moved on a while; I had run a few local trials and, although not doing anything startling, I was very much enjoying it. These sheep dog men must be of the old character type. As an example – I was at Longshaw trials, which are held on the moors above Sheffield on the boundary of Yorkshire and Derbyshire near Hathersage; it was pouring down with rain, the competitor was at the post with an army greatcoat down to his ankles and a hat which was cascading water all over him. He was not having a good time – his dog could not see the sheep at the far end of the course through the torrential rain. It would go a bit then stop, then go again and stop – the competitor was fed up and shouted to his dog, "if you can't do better than that, go home!" His dog looked at him and, not knowing what to do, started to go towards the boundary wall – then it stopped and looked back at his master, who said, "No, it's no good. Go home." The dog slunk to the surrounding wall, jumped onto it and once again looked back. The competitor, now absolutely drenched through, shouted, "No, I've had enough. Go home!" The dog disappeared over the wall. But a few seconds later, it jumped back onto it and looked, crestfallen, at his boss, who just looked at his dog for a while then said, "Ok then, let's have another go." The dog came back and they started again and managed to complete the course!

I would manage to get to one or two trials a month. To get good it would have to be at least one trial a week but two trials a week would be better. It is possible to do this if you are prepared to travel a bit. It was impossible for me, though, owing to the amount of work I had to do, So a good many of the top trialists are not sheep farmers. The top men around my area, for example, comprised a mason, a wholesale butcher, a plumbing engineer, a policeman, and a postman! There were, of course, some farmers in this position, moor shepherds Priestly, Elliot, Ollerenshaw. I only want to make these lists short as there are many others just as good, it depends on how far the area covered is; it's the mixture of the top men that I am trying to show.

One of these top men was a near neighbour of mine called Harold Loates. He was the first President of the Retford and District Sheep Dog Trials Society, and we went to a good many trials together. He helped me a lot and always wanted me to do well. At least, I think he did. One time, we were at a big trial in Lincolnshire which was running alongside the English National Ploughing Match (another love of mine). Harold had his run, which went well, and I was the next one to run. To my surprise, it went ok, that is, until I got to the pen. This is the last part of the trial where the sheep have to be put into a pen, and when the gate closes, that's the end of your run. Now, it's not far from the shedding ring (the last test before the pen) to the pen so it's usually a run to get the pen gate opened before the dog has brought the sheep. If this can be done without breaking the flow of the sheep it's usually easier (I said easier, NOT easy!) to pen. Well, I got to the pen in good time, only to find that someone had tied the pen gate with a tight knot! It's usually just lightly wound once around the gate post. Thanks, Harold.

Another time we were running at Husbands Bosworth. I was sat with Harold when my time came to run. It's about twelve yards to walk to the post, a time when nerves are still tingling. When you get to the post it's usual to settle your dog and point him in the direction in which you want him to go, then send him off when you are settled. I walked to the post, turned round to settle my dog, and IT WAS NOT THERE! A quick look around and there she was, nearly at the top of the out run about 250 yards away. My good friend Harold had kindly set her off for me, while I had been in my own world, walking to the post. Why is he still a friend?

Even though I was now enjoying trialling, the best times in working my dogs were in everyday work at home; the joy that the dogs get from working is easy to see, they just love it. It's quite often that you get a surprise. I had bought a pup from Eric, who had picked it out because its sire was Wyn Edwards' Bill. Wyn was a top man and Bill went on to win two supreme championships, so I was lucky to get this pup. I called her Trim. I must admit that I was very disappointed with her; she just would not work. It is impossible to train a dog that is not interested in sheep. You just have to wait until the dog runs at the sheep or tries to work before training can start. It's a natural instinct and it's not possible to make it happen. Trim was still with me when she was two years old (from eight weeks). I would not normally have kept her, but she loved to be in the pickup and every time I went out she would be there sitting on the front seat next to me. I guess I had got used to this; she was a good-looking bitch and a good friend but just useless. One day I wanted to get two hundred growing lambs into a pen to "dose" them for worms. They were in a fourteen-acre field and John and myself had made a pen in the field to do this. I set off from the farm with Glen in the back of the pickup to collect the lambs up and pen them. I set Glen off round the lambs, and she was about halfway round a hedgeside when I noticed another dog going round the hedgeside on the other side of the field. Now, when I was off around the sheep, all five of my dogs wanted to come with me, so I wondered which one of the ones left at home had got out and made its own way to the field? The "new" dog was going beautifully. When it got to the end of the field and met up with Glen, it turned with her and they brought the whole flock to the... pen, where I was amazed to see that the "new" dog was Trim. I felt rather foolish when I went to make sure that Trim was not still sitting in the pickup as she usually was. It was a great day or, should I say, another great day, as I had many great days with my dogs.

John, David and Helen were growing up, and Myfanwy was just like a hen with her chickens. I think that the years up to their teens were some of the happiest of our marriage. I still missed the good soil of Herefordshire. Myfanwy had a big family down there, but was so happy in Yorkshire, despite money worries, she was content bringing up her brood. At an early age, John had got an old Morris van and had taken the back off it and put a flatbed on it. He called it his "dilly" and was never happier than when taking hay out to the sheep with it; by the time he was nine he was a good driver. We were lucky that the farm was in one square block and he could drive a long way and never be anywhere near a road. David had found a good friend who lived on the next farm, and who he went to school with. Their playground covered Springs Farm and Red House Farm where many and interesting bike tracks were made. Helen had quite a difficult time as none of her classmates lived close enough to the farm to be regular visitors. Whilst looking for photographs of this time, I came across a "book" written by Helen entitled "The Story of My Life" by Helen Robinson aged eleven. She had plenty to say about living in a "desolated place"?! I must not say too much as she may take up the pen again, but it is nice to know that today, her two best friends, Joy and Ann, were in her class at Rossington Comprehensive School, even though Joy is now living in London, Ann lived in Rossington and Helen now lives in Guildford.

As time went on, Helen would often invite a boy or two or even three(?) to the farm. These lads were welcome especially at hay, harvest and dipping times, etc. Well, you've got to make the most of your assets, haven't you? It was a slack time of year when Paul arrived, but he was quite keen to help in any way, so I thought a bit of fencing would be in order. I sent Paul off with a bucket full of tools to the broken fence and said I would get over to him as soon as possible. I got there half an hour later, only to find him erecting the fence in the wrong place, so I started to remonstrate with him. At this, Paul just picked up the empty bucket and put it over his head. Well, have you ever tried telling a bucket off? Paul came to the farm many times and was a great lad.

THINGS NEVER STAY the same for very long, and Springs Farm was to alter in a big way. Mr. Toulson's firm had sold out to a bigger company and they in turn had sold out again to a bigger company. Mr. Toulson had always maintained that the farm would never be dug up for gravel; he owned the land to stop his competitors digging it up. So now we were in a different situation, and the new company wished to excavate the farm. It was agreed that fifteen acres would be worked for a start, five acres of this would be being reclaimed (i.e. put back), five acres would be being worked and five acres would be being stripped of its top soil ready to be worked. This cycle would then be repeated until the 100 acres of gravel-bearing land had been covered. You can imagine what I felt like when the first of these huge machines arrived at the farm. I had the feeling of being crushed by a great weight. I could do nothing to stop it, it rolled on, ripping up the fields, sometimes to a depth of twenty or thirty feet, other times to just a few feet, and in some places fifty feet. The machines followed the bed of gravel wherever it went.

The earlier plan of fifteen acres soon went out of the window. When the area got to about 40 acres my income was beginning to suffer badly and something had to be done. Now, when you are dealing with someone like Mr. Toulson, you make an appointment, go and see him, put your case, listen to what he says then drive the best bargain that you can. You are usually in a weak position but you do try and fight to get some satisfaction from the meeting. When dealing with a conglomerate of the size that now owned my farm, it's difficult to find a "Mr. Toulson" and you sort of follow a varying list of managers who rarely are able to take a big decision without some "higher" authority. After a mounting telephone bill, I got through to the Eastern Area Manager of the company, who, of course, did not know who I was (but at least now I had a man to write to). I was able to arrange a site meeting at my farm the next time that he was to be in my area (how big was the Eastern area?).

The day arrived and two cars made their way down my much battered drive (because of much use by twenty-ton gravel lorries) and five very smart men alighted at the farm. My greeting: "Good morning, gentlemen, would you like a cup of coffee?" was met with "No, thank you. We will get on with the job." Out came the wellingtons and we all traipsed off to the workings. It soon became obvious which one was the Eastern Manager (I had been introduced to them all by name but not by title). He listened while the local plant manager and the transport manager explained the quarry working problems before turning to the two that had come in the other car. These two were very interesting, one was a conservationist, the other a landscape agriculturist. So we had quite a high-powered group. I must make the most of it, it would not happen again. I wished that I had known beforehand who was to be there as I would have been more prepared. I had only expected the Eastern Manager to talk about compensation.. The best thing to do here was wait and see what all the others had to say. I would then know their plan and it would give me a little time to think. To them, this situation was a "temporary working" that in two years would be finished with and they would have moved on to another site. To me, it was my life and future and I would have to live with whatever they left behind. I could not do anything after they restored and left my land, so let's try and get them going in my direction.

The plant manager had his say and I had no input there, as it was the quality and quantity of the gravel that was his interest. I had been trying to catch the transport manager for some time as my "drive" was in a shocking state, but his only interest was keeping the flow of face gravel constant, so as long as his lorries could travel up and down the drive, he was happy. His drivers were on piece work, so the more loads they managed, the more wages they got. So, all day long, the drive became a race track for big lorries. There are two drives into Springs Farm off the road, so the lorries were able to come in down one and out through the other so the traffic was able to run through the farm without meeting another lorry dashing in the opposite direction. This was fine for them but it was just ruining both my drives. I had tried to get the drivers to use just one drive, and they often did for a short while, but once one had gone right though they were soon all off through again. So first thing, today, was to get the transport manager to agree in front of the Eastern Manager to use just one drive. I was surprised when this was accepted by the transport manager without objection. So far, so good.

The restoration manager explained his view of the landscaping of the site. He had recently done one similar and had been awarded a certificate by the Ministry of Agriculture, and was able to show us a picture of this (also the certificate). To say that I was unimpressed was to grossly underestimate my feelings. It was dreadful: it was a square block of dead flat land with dikes running in a herringbone fashion into a square lake in one corner of the site. It may have got the most efficient use of all the land, but I could not see any enjoyment in farming it. The financial return from farming this poor land is so small that there has to be some pleasure in farming it. He went on to say that the places that had only had four or five feet of gravel taken out would be pushed into the deep areas and a constant level could be attained at about ten feet below the old original level. A hole would then be dug right at the far end and drainage put in. Somehow I had to change his plans from this soul-destroying scheme without upsetting him. Indeed, I wanted him on my side. I thought the best approach was by assuming that the restored land was going to be used for growing crops on. I explained that once the land had been levelled, most of the area would have varying depths of covering on, what was now the bottom of the quarry floor. The variation would be from nil to thirty feet and this infill would be, to all intents and purposes, bottomless for the machines that would be travelling on it. Furthermore, we would not know, once the levelling had been done, where these variations were. It would be a nightmare, for when the land was wet a machine would sink into the depth of the old quarry floor, i.e. four feet or thirty feet. This attack was immediately followed by stating that his award-winning plan would be wonderful for stock farming, as I had no doubt that's what it was for (creep). I then pointed out the lovely roll and flow of the now quarry bottom, which, if covered to a constant depth of, say, two feet with the banks of top soil that had been stripped off at the start, would result in a workable and aesthetic area of farmland with natural deep parts that would drain most of the area. The whole hundred or so acres would look just beautiful and I had no doubt that the landscaper would win a second award for an entirely different scheme. I felt that maybe I had been too condescending, but my passion had been genuine. I could see this "moonscape" transformed into a real pastoral place, with deep green grass and contrasting white sheep, a satisfying scene. I shall ever be in debt to the conservationist at this time, for he spoke up in favour of my idea, and, in a much better way, put forward his ideas which complemented mine. I was pleased to see that the landscaper and he were enthusiastically drawing up a new plan with no flat squares but undulating landscapes. The Eastern Manager was watching me closely.

My big concern was the loss of income while the quarrying was going on. I had agreed that it would be much better to do the landscaping when the whole area had been gravelled, instead of doing it in isolated bits. So it was going to be at least four years out of production, and then there would not be much income from it short term.

One of the feed companies that came round to the farm contacted me one day and asked if I would look at some figures that a sheep farmer had given them with the object of getting credit from them until his lambs were sold. It was basically a lamb-fattening scheme for his own produced lambs. He wanted to keep his lambs instead of selling them as stores. The feed firm rep came round and asked if I would write a report on this project and send it to the head office. This was done and the next time the rep came round, I said, "I reckon you owe me a bag of sheep nuts for that report." "Ok," he said, and gave me one, so it was a bit of a surprise when a week later I received through the post a cheque for £250 from his head office! I immediately wrote back to thank them and said if I could be of help any time I would be pleased to. And so started a three-year association that just came at the right time for me. I travelled many miles for this company and in a way was sorry to leave them when my land was at last restored to a farmable state. So, by this bit of luck, we were able to survive.

JOHN WAS NOW getting old enough to be a real help on the farm. He was very useful, as one of his loves was mechanics, and I remember one holiday when he said that the clutch on the International B.250 wanted replacing – could he do it? I said, "Can you do it?" "Yes," he said. "Ok, have a go."

I spent that day spraying corn for weeds, and when I came to put the tractor away I saw John in the stone barn. He had put straw bales around the walls, and as he dismantled the tractor he had put the parts in order around the barn. The tractor itself was now in two parts – the back axle and bell housing, chocked up and held up with a jack, and the front end and engine chocked up the same – with a two-foot gap in between. I had a sinking feeling, but, "How's it going, John?" "Alright, Dad. I will want the new clutch in the morning, and I'll have it going by tomorrow night." And he did; I could not wait for him to finish school.

Although John liked his machinery, he was also becoming a good shepherd. We had gone round the sheep together for a while, and one day I suggested we go round and check the sheep. As we were walking down the drive, John said, "What are we looking for, Dad?" "Just to check that they are healthy." It's a job to say what you see when you look over a gate at 200 sheep. You do not see each individual sheep, at least not to "check" each one. Your eye travels over the whole flock and just stops at the sheep that's not right. It stands out like a sore thumb. Then it's put the dog round, quietly get the crook around its back leg and catch it (and hope you have got the right one!). Then treat it. There are usually one or two in each flock to do each night. John was quick to learn this and at lambing time he was better than me at getting a "stuck" lamb born. These skills were a great help and saved us a lot of money paying for mechanics and vets.

In going to sheep dog trials, patience is learned because if sheep are pushed too hard they will "break" and points and time are lost, so in the shedding ring and at the pen, the quieter the better. I was glad to have learned this lesson when one day we were dipping. It had been a long hard day and we were down to the last thirty or forty when a hurdle broke and the sheep were out. The big flock that had been dipped were out in the front meadow, a field of eighteen acres. The undipped sheep were now off around the buildings to join them. I dashed through the buildings, calling for Trim, hoping to cut them off before they got mixed up. I nearly managed this, but not quite; about fifteen had got through into the field with the dipped sheep. I slammed the gate shut as I ran through, then stopped, got Trim to my side and quietly walked past a group of about fifty sheep, with the undipped ones mixed with them. I kept walking away from the farm, driving the dipped sheep as far away as I could, then I turned round to face the fifty bunch and started to drive them back towards the farm. As I slowly made my way back, I was able to let the dipped sheep past me a few at a time to join the others. As the flock got smaller it was a case of letting one or two back. This was all done slowly and quietly and the sheep behind me were stopping and grazing so they were not panicking the small flock (they were, of course, hungry as they had been in the pens most of the day). When I got back to the gate, it was opened again and the undipped sheep were once again penned at the dip. I managed to get the last two dipped sheep away and arrived with just the fifteen undipped ones. As I walked through the gate with them, a group of people started to clap. They were on the road and had been watching the whole affair. Even though I was tired, I felt so proud of my dog.

The gravelling came to an end, and by making a friend of both the machine driver and the landscape man, we finished up with a job that was as good as it could be. I got my undulating landscape and when the grass grew on it the moonscape of the last four years was, at last, a thing of the past. The only thing was I had not yet been paid my compensation. You will be able to guess that one or two letters had been sent but the company were "dragging their feet". As we were into the second year from the activity of gravelling, I thought I was being hard done by. We were trimming some ewes' feet, which, believe me, is a dirty, smelly job, when Myfanwy called out to say that the Eastern Area Manager was on the phone. It was a really bad time for me but, filthy and smelly, I went to talk to him. "Trevor, I have been looking at this compensation. What would you say if I offered you the house and buildings instead of paying you?"

Now this was a crafty move on their part, as the house and buildings had to be kept in good repair, so cost them money. Now the reason for them owning the farm had gone, as there was no more gravel left for them to dig, the farm was going to cost them money. My new rent for the gravelled hundred or so acres was nothing for four years and then less than two pounds per acre after that. A huge conglomerate would want to be rid. So my answer was, "If you throw in the gravelled land I would say yes." – A long pause – "I cannot do that, it would have to go to the company." Me – "How long will that take?" – "About a fortnight" – "I may have changed my mind by then" – "Good grief, Trevor, I was only ringing to see if you were interested, not to make a deal" – "Ok, ring me when you can offer me a deal." It was the following day at lunchtime that he rang. "Trevor, I cannot do it, but what I can do is to square the land off, which will give you your drive to the road, with the house, buildings and four acres of land round it to connect you to the drive. This will cost you £12,000."

It was now my turn for a long pause. – "Make it £8,000 and we've got a deal." Where the heck I was going to get £8,000 I do not know, so it was somewhat of a relief when he said, "Sorry, I can't take that." I had mixed feelings when I said, "Ok, let's get back to you paying me instead of me paying you." I knew that my bank manager would be better pleased, but it was not to be just yet. "Trevor, I have just had the nod from my director, we can go ahead at £8,000, are you still on?" – "Yes," I said.

The Eastern Manager told me later that he had never had such an exciting day in his life; he could not believe what was happening.

Trim had by now grown into a good trial dog. I had been training her for twenty minutes night and morning for some time and she was as good as she was going to get. We had been to quite a few trials and I was now enjoying them. I knew that I had not much chance of winning, so my pleasure was in beating the top men. Often, these men would be giving experience to a young dog, or bringing on new dog, so it was sometimes possible to beat them.

One of my great days was to beat Norman Darrel the postman. He was a super trials man, so that day was one of my highlights. But really, the one man I wanted to beat was, of course, Harold Loates, my neighbour and best friend. We had been to many trials together and I had always been "miles" behind him, but as Harold had won the English National, this was not surprising. We, that is, the Retford and District Trials Society, put on an open trial at Osberton Estate in Nottinghamshire every year. It's a wonderful place to have a trial – it's in the Dukeries, just perfect. It's a big course and most of the top trialists come to enjoy its challenge. As I was on the committee, I ran Trim early in the morning as it was a busy day for me, and once the trial was underway I would have no time to run later.

Trim did so well, a good outrun, picked up the sheep, brought them quietly through the fetch gates and down to me. This was a good start and I did not want to waste it, so I slowed down a bit and took the sheep through the drive gate then across the drive and through the gates and back to me. Missed nothing, wonderful. I went very carefully into the ring to shed off my sheep (this is where the sheep have to be kept in a 30-yard-diameter, sawdust-marked ring and one cut off and held apart from the others without going out of the ring). It took me a while as I did not want to spoil things now with only the pen to do. I got my sheep cut off, got the ok from the judges, and went to the pen. At previous trials, I had found to my cost that if the sheep once get away and go round the pen, it's an awful job to stop them doing it again. So, steady now, don't push too hard. The first sheep goes into the pen and the rest follow it – bang goes the pen gate – I had finished without one mistake. Now this was the first time that I had ever done this; it was a great feeling, especially at this big Osberton Trial. I shall remember that twenty minutes for all my life. Now this run did not mean that I had got full points. Far from it – every bend and hesitation would lose points. If the dog over ran, points would go, so even though all the obstacles had been overcome without loss, I knew points had been lost. Harold ran soon after and had a good run but missed the drive gate and did not shed at the first attempt. He came up to me and said, "Well, at last you have done it, you've beaten me"(!) He had a big grin on his face and shook my hand. Now, it's funny really, I just happened to be outside the Secretary's tent when the points were put up, with Harold at my side. So how many did I beat him by? Well, Harold Loates 84 points, Trevor Robinson 77. Harold now looked at me with an even bigger smile on his face. "Never mind, Trevor, you'll do it one day." But I never did.

I have never disputed a trials judge ever, and never would, but after the end of the day, I asked the judge where had I lost my points. He said, "Trevor, you did very well but you did it without STYLE." I guess I'm just a working farmer!

MONEY HAD BEEN gathered together to buy the farm; all my small savings plans for my pension had been cashed up and yet another loan from the bank had been arranged. It was a good feeling to now own a part of my farm, my farmhouse and buildings, as when you are a tenant there is always the problem of retirement – a home has to be found, even if you were hoping to hand over the tenancy to your son. We were now safe from this, as on the land I had bought there was a bungalow which was to become John's home when he got married, which he did in 1978. It was to be nine years before we got our first grandchild, Paul.

David was to leave school in 1971; he was a quiet lad and we thought that if he came to work at home he would very soon become an introvert, so we bought him a moped and off he went to work for Doncaster Parks Department. They have been super with him and he is still there thirty-three years later.

Helen – I can never understand her – went to Wisbech

College to learn flower arranging. I can understand that, but then to practise this in London is just beyond me.

Myfanwy was the rock of the family, calm through everything. She had started spinning and had spun and knitted me a pullover from a particular sheep of ours that had a nice fleece. It was rather an odd shape and itched like mad, but it was all her own work. She was now also enjoying the WI and baked for their stall in Retford Market, but she was still never happier than when all our family were at home together.

The Longshaw Sheep Dog Trials Society goes back over 100 years. It's lasted so long, I think, because it's in sheep country, high up where the Derbyshire moors meet the Yorkshire moors; the men who farm up here are true sheep men, it's their whole life and their local rivalry is unending, so I would think it will go on for a long time yet. When England, Ireland, Scotland and Wales started to compete against one another, the International came to be run in the first week of September. This enabled the national teams to compete and select men and dogs to get their best teams together during the open season, i.e. April–September. (During the winter months it's usual to run "nursery" trials, where young novice dogs are started.) Now, Longshaw Trials are run the first week in September so there is a clash. Longshaw is where everyone wants to win, so if someone is selected to run in the

International they may not get to run at Longshaw. When the International asked Longshaw to move their date the answer was no, as it had been at this time for years, so it was staying there. You would have thought that the International would have tempted the top men and Longshaw would have suffered, but it's not happened. Longshaw still thrives, which shows what a good trial it is, and the quality of the men who run it.

Harold has won Longshaw; first prize used to be a silver teapot! Brilliant, these lads like to be practical. I have run there but never for more than five minutes at a time, but even for that short time it's a wonderful feeling. Longshaw holds another trial in May when the nursery dogs are at their best. The first prize is the Bolton Cup, which is the tallest cup (two feet high) in trialling, I believe. Harold has also won this cup for a novice dog (i.e. a dog that has never won). Since Harold told me about it, I wanted to try and win it and I now had a dog that might be able to do it, so I started practising. Back to twice a day in two twenty-minute stints, as well as taking her to various locations to get her used to running away from home. I expect Trim often wished she had never jumped out of my pickup that day when she first showed interest, though I must say that she has never stopped since.

The great day arrived and Myfanwy said that she had never seen me so nervous. I went out at 6 a.m. to give Trim a run – it was hopeless, at first I could not even whistle! Not a sound, then twice I gave her the wrong command. I finished up a nervous wreck and the dog was in a flat spin. Myfanwy said, "Best stop at home, love." Not likely – I had been working too hard for too long for that. So I got to Bamford, where the trial was to be, at 8 a.m. I was not the first by a long way. By 9 a.m. we were all there and had to draw lots to get our running order. I was running about halfway down the list, which was about 12.30 p.m. I had a long wait. Harold and Barbara Sykes (the Retford Secretary) were there to support me (they had both won the cup), as were most of the Retford Society.

As I was walking round the trials field before running, a young lad said to me, "Are you running?" "Yes," I said. "When you have run will you let me have a go with your dog?" I said, "Yes, you can go and run for me if you like." "No," he said, "I've never run a dog." So I had not got out of running, but at that moment I could have run away.

My turn arrived, and with a great show of bravado I strode to the post. I thought that whatever I did I must do it with STYLE. I had a good start – Trim usually started well – with the outrun and lift, and through the fetch gates. Down to me and round me and off on the drive, still ok. Cross-drive a bit off-line but through the gates and back to me. As the dog is bringing the sheep to you from the last drive gates, it's a natural thing for the dog to do, i.e. bring the sheep to you, so I had a second or two to notice that all the spectators were watching. If I had been making a mess most people would not have been interested, so I must be doing ok. Now for the shed. There was no sawdust ring as this was a novice trial, just a clean cut straight through the middle, two on each side. This was done alright, so now a good finish at the pen was required. A voice boomed out from the spectators: "Now get 'em penned, Robinson." So I did. It was all over in a quarter of an hour. I had spent three times that every day for months, but at least I had not let my dog down. I did not know how many points I had got and would not know until about 4 p.m. as the points are not put up in an open trial.

It was a long three-and-a-half hours. I had gone over my run many times and tried to judge it against the others, but it was impossible. So we had to wait, but it was worth it. I had to carry that two-foot-high cup home and keep it for a year. Another job for Myfanwy to clean, but I think that she was pleased.

Just before going home that May afternoon, the sheep had to be taken back to the grazing field. I asked if I could do it – a young lad worked my dog for me – I hope it gave him a start, for it's a fine sport.

AT LONG LAST we were feeling a bit more secure at Springs Farm; the days when the bailiff called me Trevor were now a thing of the past, although I shall never forget the many times when the bailiff had rung me up, from Doncaster, to say that he would be calling round in the morning to deliver a Court Order, but should I happen to be out he would not be able to get round again for two weeks. This was a great help to me as I would at once contact the creditor and arrange a settlement without paying the court costs. I had walked along this tightrope for a few years, especially after the accident with the combine. The bailiff was a good friend to me, as were my many longsuffering creditors, but with their help I was able to pay every penny that I owed. And it was a wonderful time when at last this day came.

I was also able to look back on the time when we were down to our last ten shilling note. Myfanwy put it behind the clock in the kitchen and we looked at it for a week. Then I said, "Let's go out and have a meal." We went to the Crown at Bawtry and had a really good meal. Then we came home and we had now got nothing!

Then there was the time when I wanted some cash from the bank, which would push me over my overdraft, so I took John into Doncaster with me. I told him to go into the bank and see if the manager was at his desk in his office (this could be seen from the counter). He came out and said no, he was not in, so in I went to cash my cheque. As I walked through the door, I came face to face with the manager! "Good morning, Trevor, how are you?" – "Fine, sir, thank you. I look forward to seeing you on the farm next month." – "Yes, I hope it looks well." Phew! These days are good to look back on, but at the time it was both wearing and desperate. So now things were easier we could buy a new washing machine or tractor if we needed one. My rule of thinking what we could do without and not what we could do with had at last paid off.

It was at this time that my fortune took a very bad turn for the worse. Myfanwy became ill with cancer. She had had a mastectomy twenty years before but we had got through that, so it was a blow after all this time to tackle cancer again. She did not want to go into hospital, she wanted to stay on the farm, so she did. We went through sixteen months of chemotherapy, but to no avail. Our daughter Helen came home from London to help me look after her. Helen's boss in London said she had to stay as long as needed, her job would still be there, no matter how long it was; a good man, Mr. Davison.

This is a time that is not easy to write about, so please excuse me. Myfanwy did get great strength from her religion and tender care from Helen and friends. We went to Sheffield for chemotherapy, always with hope, but the last week of March, we were told that this would be the last time as there was no point in carrying on as the cancer was now too widespread. The surgeons had done all that they could. We were told that Myfanwy would have a pain-free last few weeks. How did I drive home to the farm after this news? Chemo had always had a bad effect but we could always say "let's grin and bear it, and when you are better we will do this or that." But now there was nothing to say, just deep, deep love to see us through. Myfanwy died on September the first – the last six weeks of her life she had gone blind. She died at home on the farm with John, David, Helen, her sister Beth and myself at her side. It did not surprise me when, that evening, there was the most glorious sunset that I have ever seen, set over the farm. I looked back over the 37 years that we had been together and remembered all the hard years that we had been through – the constant struggle with lack of money – the determination to have our own farm – the joy of bringing up our daughter and two sons – the many, many good friends that we had made. It was so sad that Myfanwy should die just when life was being kinder to us.

It was in those last weeks that she said, "We've had a wonderful life together."

Post Script

AFTER WRITING THE last chapter, I put my pen down, as I could not write any more. It seemed to be the right place to finish, as it was the climax of my ambition as a farmer. From then on, my life took a different course. But I did not want to finish on a sad note, so maybe you would like to know how life carried on.

During the last few weeks of Myfanwy's life, her sister Beth came to stay at the farm to help me. Beth had been a sister (medical) during the war, so she was a great help with giving Myfanwy just the correct amount of morphine to keep the pain at bay and allow Myfanwy to still be lucid. Another person who came to help was Helen, the daughter of Mum and Dad's best friend. Helen had just got back to England after being in Australia for a big adventure, where she had gone to teach for two years but had stayed for twelve! Helen and her Mum and Dad had spent many weeks at the farm, coming for holidays and weekends throughout her childhood. She was now applying for a teaching post in England, so she was able to come and help with cooking and housework. As you will understand, I was finding the situation very stressful, so this help was very much appreciated.

After Myfanwy's death, it was back to farming and looking after David, my second son, who was still living at home. John had had the "brunt" of the farm work to do for quite a long time now, and was very capable, doing a good job. My life had lost its spark; with Beth and Helen now gone and my daughter Helen back at work in London, I was pretty low. Making meals for David and myself was a pain, but I bought a deep-fat fryer and we lived on fried chips with egg – fish –

corned beef, etc. So although we had hot meals, it was not very good. This came to an end when the fryer caught fire and we nearly burnt the kitchen out! Not wanting a repeat of this, I bought a microwave and eating habits became a bit healthier.

Helen (not my daughter) had now got a teaching post at Ellerslie in Malvern, a small girls' independent school, but she still kept in touch and came up to the farm on one of her "leave out" weekends. We went for a walk around the farm with all the dogs, and it was just great; I don't know whether the sun was shining or not but it certainly seemed so. It was a special time for me, life seemed to be worth living again and I knew at that moment I had fallen in love again, a situation that I never would have thought could happen. What should I do? If you remember, Helen came to Buckfield when she was seven years old to see Myfanwy and John, our newborn baby, when I was twenty-one years old, so better say nothing. Our walk continued and Helen wanted to know all about what was happening; she said that the time that she had spent on the farm looking after Myfanwy and me had been special and she missed it now being away. At this moment, our hands touched and a feeling like an electric shock was felt by both of us (it's never happened since!?). We kissed.

Now I am in a unplanned situation, to be honest, in a flat spin. My life has never been "humdrum" but this is something different; I have always known where I wish to go, even if it's unattainable for a while, but now I don't know what to do. Helen has a good job in Malvern, she is a spinster with no ties. I have a farm, two sons and a daughter. I am no good on my own. I can work all day on my own but am just lost in the farmhouse with no company. So first, what does John think? He is happy to take on the farm – he thinks he would manage it ok (thinks he could have farmed it better than me for the last fifteen years!). So that's ok. David would live with John and Elaine and would be fine. Daughter Helen is a problem – although she has been away from home for a few years, Mum

Dad and farm are still important. She is devastated by my news and all is not well. She and Alistair (fiancé) think it's far too soon after Myfanwy's death. I think so too, but I know that Myfanwy would be pleased. If the situation were the other way round, I would be pleased for her. We knew one another well and it would be a comfort to know that the one left behind would be looked after and loved. We had one saving grace, and that was that daughter Helen and Helen were, and had been all their lives, good friends. They were able to talk to one another and daughter slowly was won over, although she was to suffer, unbeknown to me, for a long time.

So we now have a plan – we will get married – John and David will stay at the farm – I will move to Malvern, where I will rent some land and keep a flock of ewes – Helen will keep her job at Ellerslie and daughter will give us her blessing, without which I could not have got married.

Leaving the farm was a big "wrench". You will understand that it had been my whole life for 30-odd years. We moved into a "chocolate box" black-and-white half-timbered cottage in Herefordshire. It was good to be back in Herefordshire and strange to be married a second time down here, even though I had spent most of my life in Yorkshire. I have only had one pair of black shoes in my whole life, so I was married wearing these shoes twice with a gap of 36 years! I still have them. I set about getting some land to start a small flock, but was having quite a job to find some; it seemed as though this Yorkshire man was not in favour, that is, until the day of the local sheep dog trial at Cradley. I entered the trial, and after it I was offered several blocks of land, so I was at last able to get my sheep, a flock of 135 North Country mules. I found it most odd to get up and have breakfast without doing 2½ to 3 hours of work first. But I soon got to enjoying my small flock and spent the next three years doing this, with Helen going off to Ellerslie each morning.

There always seems to be some event that sets us off in

another direction, even when you think that you are settled. Well, this happened to us again. Ellerslie and Malvern College joined together to become one school. So it was now Malvern College, a co-ed school. It was soon after this that Helen was made a Housemistress; this meant that we would have to move into a house in Malvern College and look after sixty girls living with US! So the sheep went and Helen, myself and Tresta – my last sheep dog – moved into the college – which was very odd as I had always wanted to go to college!

So how did an old shepherd fare? Well, the first two years were pretty bad – it just was not my environment at all, but Tresta just loved it! She was spoiled rotten and even had two litters of pups while she was there. The last night of the term before Christmas was always a very exciting time for the girls – Christmas Dinner! After the meal, each year group would do an entertainment and the staff did theirs first. One year a colleague gave Helen a poem as written by a dog – but I thought a genuine article would be better and this poem has been on the dining room wall ever since.

TRESTA

She lives in No. Four, with her nose against the door
Waiting for a friend, to pat and stroke once more.
She will, no doubt, remember the days upon the hill
When her body was lithe and slender and youth was with her still.

The days upon the trial field she also will recall
When small success made her master ten feet tall.
With forty years of breeding in her long pedigree
She had to be the best, and so she proved to be.

Then came the time for breeding with puppies by the score
When some top handlers were crying out for more.
Top dogs in Wales and Scotland came from her litters too
Her wonderful temperament always showing through.

She was made redundant from the workday load
And moved to Malvern College just down along the road
Where visitors are welcomed by a wagging tail
And Tresta's lovely nature does not often fail.

She loves to meet new pupils, and help them settle in,
If they are a little homesick, their hearts she's sure to win.
And a walk along the Common does wonders for the pair
With the burden lightened, knowing that we care.

Tresta's ageing body is nowadays kept in trim
By Miss Scott's early morning walk in light that's often dim.
Now her eyes are pale and fading, her muzzle has gone grey
But, she's still quite healthy and has not "had her day".

So, raise your glass to Tresta,
the best friend in the world
and thank her for HER friendship
whilst in her box she's curled.

As time went on, I came to enjoy the constant flow of
pupils that came to No. 4, and appreciated the work done by

Helen and her staff. Helen badgered me into starting a girls' cricket team (she was also head of Physical Education), which was a riot, as eight of that first team were German girls, and their parents were walking around the field saying, it's nice but how do they score the goals?! We have been in No. 4 now for 11 years and Helen is due to retire in August, when we will move into an old black-and-white house in Herefordshire. Unfortunately, we will not be taking Tresta with us as she died in the tenth year.

A Tribute to my Wonderful Dogs

EVERY YEAR I used to go to Scotland to buy sheep in August. I always took a dog with me and went around the various sheep dog trials and tried my luck at winning a few pounds off my Scottish friends. I never managed to win any money off them. I always said it was because they did not like Scottish pounds going over the border! They said I wasn't good enough. At any rate, at a trial at Nethy Bridge, I saw a dog called Queen run and, believe me, she was well named – she had style, grace, balance, a good "eye" and she was fast. I thought that her bloodline would improve my breeding stock no end. So I had a word with Alex Hughson, who came from an island called Fetlar in Shetland, and learned that he was going to breed with her on his return to Fetlar and he would save a pup for me. It was two years before I received the phone call to say my pup was ready and what should they call it? Just off the coast of Fetlar there is a group of rocks called the Skerries, so I called her Skerry. I had a 450-mile journey from the farm to Aberdeen to collect her from the Shetland Ferry.

We drew on to the wharf just as the ferry arrived – great timing – and I said to the seaman that I had come to collect a sheepdog. His reply was "There's no dog on this ferry", to which I replied, "are you sure?" Yes was his reply – come and see – all the kennels are empty. So, with a sinking heart, I went to ring up Alex to ask what had gone wrong. Nothing, he said – I put her on the ferry at Lerwick and as the next docking is Aberdeen, she must be there. So, back to the ferryman, who was mystified. "I'll go and ask the Captain." And off he went. It was not long before he returned with a big grin on his face, carrying "Skerry" and saying, "This is no a dog, it's a wee pup!"

What a relief! It appears that the Captain had the pup with him in his cabin for the whole of the journey.

She had had a 14-hour sea journey from Lerwick and she was just eight weeks old. She was borne home to the farm with joy, and during the next two years she matured into a great dog.

It was at this time that my fortune took a very bad turn for the worse. My wife, Myfanwy, became ill with cancer and the next two years were taken up running the farm and nursing her, no time or inclination for sheep dog trialling. I knew Skerry was ready to trial, and I also knew that she was very good. It was a great sadness to me to let her go, but I had a good friend and neighbour that I went to trials with called Harold Loates. I knew that if he had her, she would be well looked after and he would take her to the top, as he was a far better handler at trials than I was. So Skerry went to Harold and I am proud to say that they became well known throughout the British Isles. In her first year of trialling, they won fourteen first prizes! They also became well known when she was narrowly beaten in the final of One Man and His Dog on television by an exceptionally good dog from Wales. It was two years after I had married Helen, following the death of Myfanwy, that I received a phone call from Harold saying Skerry had just had pups and he guessed he owed me one, what should he call it? He did not owe me anything, but it was a wonderful surprise for me. So I said to call her Tresta. This is the name of the farm on Fetlar where Skerry was born. So Tresta came down to Herefordshire, where I had a small flock of 130 sheep, my farm in Yorkshire having been handed over to my son on my marriage to Helen.

So, once again it was back to training a dog from the line of Queen all those years ago – an extra special feeling. Once again, I got as far as two years into training when Helen became a housemistress in Malvern College. This in turn meant we had to live in at the College so the sheep had to go. What about the dog? It was a gamble. Should a farm dog be taken from its environment and live in a house instead of its kennel? Although she is a very kind dog, is there a possibility of her biting a pupil? In the end, it is my selfishness that says I will feel a lot better if my dog comes with me. So Tresta comes to school to hold my hand! In two weeks she settled in; it took me at least two years. She is a huge success, I am not. Most importantly, she is happy – she just loves it. She gets stroked and patted all the time, particularly by Enid, our housekeeper, who loves her and spoils her. Girls hang onto her when they are homesick and somehow feel better because she is there. She is part of No. 4.

Just once in ten years a boy took a kick at her. Unfortunately for the young man, I was near. He had not gone twenty paces before I was at his side. I told him it would have been better to kick me rather than my dog. He was told that she was worth more than him – she had more brains than he and she was certainly much prettier as well, so he was definitely on a loser. That is the only bad instance, as far as I know, and he insisted he was taking a fling kick at nothing and just happened to be by the dog. After being told this several times, weeks later I think he is telling the truth, and I never could see why anyone would want to kick a dog.

I was always sensitive as to whether the girls, and indeed, the college would accept a dog in the boarding house, but I need not have worried as both were fine, and at one time, housemasters were encouraged to keep a dog. So Tresta settled down to a life of luxury, playing with the boys of No. 7 on the tennis courts. I did not feel too comfortable when she took to playing "ball", but she was very happy. I do think that she helped with the feeling of being a family. It is a lovely atmosphere in the house and Tresta made it more "homely". We were lucky that this situation carried on for ten years. We had known for some time that she was unwell and this Easter she was in pain and, at 14 years of age, could not and should not be allowed to suffer. So, with the help of Martin Knott, an ex-Deputy Head of the College, she was quietly put to sleep. She will be missed.

Life Without Sheepdogs

TRESTA WAS MY last dog – I always said that I would not have a dog when I had no sheep – it would be wrong for me to enjoy a dog's companionship when it would be unable to do what it really enjoyed most – working sheep. (I am only able to recognise one breed, you understand!) So, since retiring, my pleasure has been in watching my family growing up.

John, my elder son had, to wait nine years before having a son himself, Paul, despite the help of medicines and IVF. Elaine lost faith in them, gave them all up – and yes, she conceived soon after! Tragically, she died when Paul was a teenager and John was lucky to meet Ann several years later and is now very happily married and is farming Springs Farm really well. Paul, my grandson, is a mechanic, working on Volvo engines and he loves to be at Springs Farm. He would dearly like to farm with his dad but the total income would not be enough – and as he has now become a dad himself, this is even more unlikely. So I am now a great-grandad – heck! David, John's brother, lives in a mobile home on the farm, still working for Doncaster Council in their Parks Department – his one and only job since he left school at 16. He has just five years to go to retirement… which makes me feel even older!

Let me tell you about Helen, our youngest. She had worked in London and America as a florist before going to work with her partner, Alistair, in a picture-framing business in Guildford, Surrey. They are now highly regarded bespoke picture framers and have worked on some rather strange "pictures". One was a squash racquet, another an army greatcoat jacket 5ft. long. there have been many a dozen football shirts, some signed by top premier league stars and a huge picture of Concorde, which was to be hung in BA's Head Office. However, when it was delivered ready framed, it was too big to go through the door so they had to take it home and cut it in half... so if you ever have anything odd to frame, you know where to go?! They have been doing this sort of work for 25 years now and this year celebrate their silver wedding... it's that time thing again!

During this time, they have brought up two lovely girls, Katie, who is 23, and Alex, who is in her last year at university and about to be 21. When Katie graduated with an English degree, she managed to get a job at Waterstones (could this be useful, I ask?), although she really wants to get into the political world, which may well be a tricky nut to crack. Alex is a talented sportswoman who is good at netball and football. She has done work experience placements at Crystal Palace and the Surrey FA and recently got her first FA coaches Grade 1 award. She and her Dad, a football referee, are passionate Liverpool supporters so are happy with their team at present. Alex plans to go to Camp America, working with young people, when she graduates in a few months' time.

That just leaves this person I have now known for 69 years – but had to "put up with" for the last 27 of them as a wife. Despite this mammoth burden of age, she is very active playing tennis, rambling, swimming, playing bridge, singing in various choirs, bell ringing – and also Hon. Sec. of the WI! I do see her occasionally, fortunately, at some meal times when she is able to tell me what chore to do next... usually peeling potatoes or vacuuming the house. So, I suppose life is now "normal", a situation I hope will last a few years yet.

Those last words of Myfanwy, "we have had a good life" still hold true.